MW00657647

THROUGH THE IMPOSSIBLE

Lessons in Caregiving
From a Husband Who's Been There

Matthew Ames

IBIS BOOKS

Published by Ibis Books, 2349 Hyde Park Street, Sarasota, FL, 34239.

Cover Design by 100Covers

Illustrations by Levi DeMatteo

First edition, 2023

ISBN-13: 978-1-956672-17-6 (Ebook edition)

ISBN-13: 978-1-956672-18-3 (Paperback edition)

Contents

Foreword VI

Part One: Our Story

1. The Call 3
2. Liz 6
3. The Warning Signs 13
4. Appendiceal Adenocarcinoma 19
5. The High Grade 25
6. Mapping Out a Treatment Plan 29
7. Grinding Through the Summer 35
8. Bracing for the Main Event 43
9. The Surgery and the Aftermath 49
10. Coming Home 59
11. Released Into the Wild 67

Part Two: What I've Learned

12. An Update and a Disclaimer 77
13. Taking Care of Yourself 83

14. Simplifying Your Life 127
15. Practice Thankfulness 152
16. Have Faith 176
17. A Closing Note About Closure 187
Acknowledgements 191
About the Author 197

To Liz

Foreword

One of the first things I said to my husband Matt when I realized the gravity of our situation was, "I wouldn't want to be in your shoes." See, all I had to do was fight cancer. But he not only had to fight cancer, he had to take care of our kids, continue his law practice, and do all the other things that keep a household running. While I, in my sorrow, got to collapse into a puddle on the ground, he had to be the rock. And the entertainment. And the levity. All while dealing with the profound feeling of helplessness that caregivers go through.

From the outside looking in, no one would have thought being a caregiver was challenging for my husband. He took on the role with endless energy, humor, and dedication. Each of these traits made being a cancer patient (and the kids of a cancer patient) tolerable. As frightening and difficult as those times were, I now look back on them in awe. Because we *lived.* We smiled. We had fun. We chose to enjoy every single day, even the particularly bad ones that required way more dad jokes than anyone could ever need. But that spirit was all we had. We didn't know if better days were ahead, so we had to make each one count.

When you are in the fight of your life, you don't have the time or bandwidth to think about what life will look like once the battle finishes. Life will just go back to normal, or so you assume. This book sheds light on the fact that life after trauma is anything but normal. In fact, once the traumatic event ends, the emotional journey has just begun. The survivor and caregivers can't just pick things up and continue on the tried-and-true path. No.

They are released into the wild. Unchartered territory.

Everything is unfamiliar, and questions abound. Where do we go? Back to our old life, like nothing happened? Impossible. So do we create an entirely new life? Or some sort of hybrid? How much time do we have left together? A year, five years, or fifty? Should we spend all our money now or save for our future? Do we quit our jobs and take our kids out of school, or do we try to live a normal life? And, honestly, what even *is* a "normal" life?

With rare cancer like mine, you wrestle with these questions while carrying the weight of knowing that more cancer may lurk right around the corner. I liken it to being forced to wear a bomb vest that you don't know when or if it will explode. This journey of ours—being released into the wild—has been a secret struggle that warrants talking about. This journey has also made our family's priorities crystal clear and solidified the way we want to live our lives. This clarity is what Matt hopes his book can bring to others, and maybe save them a few steps of the trauma it takes to get there.

Matt used to tell me, “Being a caregiver to you is my proudest role.” He wore this title like a badge of honor. It wasn’t always easy to hear, because nobody likes to think they need this kind of support. But sometimes you find yourself in situations that you never would have dreamt of for yourself. And so I am profoundly thankful that I had Matt to take on that role. I believe that our success—both with battling cancer and building a full life—is due to the perspective and lessons he has captured in this book.

As Matt notes, life can be messy and unpredictable. No matter your struggle—be it cancer, depression, a divorce, or some other major trauma or setback—the takeaways from this book apply to all of them. If you can apply any piece of Matt’s advice to your day-to-day life, I promise your world will be a little brighter.

I know mine is.

Elizabeth (Liz) Ames

Atlanta, July 2023

Part One

OUR STORY

You're facing down

A dark hall

I'll grab my light

And go with you

"My Blood" by Twenty One Pilots

Chapter 1
The Call

ONE OF THE MOST extraordinary aspects of going through a seismic, life-changing event is how the seemingly mundane details in the moment right beforehand get permanently frozen in your mind, like a time capsule. You re-live those moments repeatedly with astonishment at how everything can change so quickly and unexpectedly.

And so it is with the morning of July 2, 2019.

It was a Tuesday, just a few weeks before my wife Elizabeth's 39th birthday, and the day began in unremarkable fashion. Our dearest out-of-town friends, the Broitman family, had just left after spending a long weekend with us at our cozy little cabin in the North Georgia mountains. We had a short work week in front of us, as we were planning to go right back up to the cabin for the July 4th holiday. Liz and I stood in the kitchen and went through the usual *here's what I've got going on today* routine. Our sons Eli and Isaac–six and three, respectively–were buzzing around in the background.

I was going straight to work with a stop at the gym on the way home, while Liz was heading in to her office but with a stop along the way at a doctor's appointment. She had an upcoming hernia repair surgery, and—as a purely precautionary measure—had scheduled a scan to make sure there weren't any other problems or surprises with her abdomen. She figured that after wrapping up her appointment, she'd be in her office by late morning. She was wearing a new purple blouse and wanted to know what I thought. I told her she looked beautiful and I loved her and was looking forward to seeing her at home at the end of the day. Then we kissed goodbye and both headed off to the day ahead.

***

There's a small law library right outside my office at work. The ongoing joke is that I've claimed it as my satellite office because whenever I am working on a large, complex case with lots of paperwork, all of my stuff ends up migrating in there. And so on this day, still well before lunchtime, I was in my "satellite office" with two young associates, Jena and Whitney, to discuss a tedious document review project in a tough business dispute we were handling. There were notepads and thick black binders spread all around us. We were midway through our long list of tasks for the morning when my legal assistant, Joanne, rushed in.

"Liz is on hold. She said it's important." I excused myself and went across the hall into my office.

I could tell from her breathing on the other end of the phone, before she'd uttered a single word, that something was seriously wrong.

"I need you to come here right now. I'm at the hospital for my scan."

"Liz? What's wrong? Are you ok?"

And it was then, through tears and labored breaths, on this otherwise ordinary day, that my wife told me she had cancer.

Chapter 2
Liz

So there is some background on Liz that is probably in order before returning to the events of July 2, 2019. She was born and raised in Newnan, Georgia, which, as I often say, is about 45 minutes south of Atlanta but also a million miles away.

This is not a backhanded slight against Newnan. Far from it. It is referred to as the "City of Homes" and the description is fitting. It is an idyllic community filled with inviting front porches facing wide rural streets. When you're there, it feels like everybody either knows each other or is connected at most by one or two degrees of separation. To this point, Liz and I once attended a real estate closing in Newnan, and to our surprise, the closing attorney ended up being an older gentleman who had known Liz since she was a child.

Newnan is polite and neighborly and overflowing with Southern warmth and charm. It is, to many, an attractive way to live in relative proximity to Atlanta but at a more relaxed pace, and without all the attendant noise, traffic, and other big city trappings.

Because of that proximity, Liz grew up enjoying the best of both worlds.

After graduating from Newnan High, she attended college in Athens, Georgia, and then obtained her law degree from Georgia State University in Atlanta. She has an oversized thirst for adventure and has traveled to faraway places across several continents, but she has also never lived more than a few hours away from the town where she was born. Even when she is in the city, she is never far from her Newnan roots.

Liz's graceful balancing of "one foot in each world" is one of the many unique and special things about her. No doubt she appreciates the ethos of small town living, but she also delights in the faster pace and lifestyle of city living. In a time when it sometimes feels like we are living in two starkly different and divided Americas, Liz is the semi-rare individual who genuinely appreciates and deftly navigates both sides of most things.

This is true for her both personally and professionally. She got her first job as a teenager, and has gone from waiting tables at a greasy spoon to serving as compliance counsel for Fortune 500 companies. She is equally comfortable and fluent in the corporate boardroom in her sharpest dark navy power suit as she is out on the construction site with hardhat and steel-tipped boots (which she proudly owns). This versatility has served her well professionally—for years, she flourished in the male-dominated construction industry—and it also brings an uncommonly deep perspective to her everyday life. Whatever the setting, Liz effortlessly adapts.

I love all of this about her.

Another thing to know about Liz is that she is a ferocious competitor, especially with endurance sports. Her competitive streak started in high school—back when she would lift weights and run stadium drills with the football team—and has been hardwired into her ever since. She has trained for and completed several marathons. She is a serious cyclist. And, for good measure, she has competed in triathlons, tough mudders, and many other racing adventures. Even while practicing law, she moonlighted as a weekend boot camp instructor. If you exclude professional athletes and grade her on a curve against other weekend-warrior types, Liz skews elite. And when you see her, you know it.

We met while Liz was still in law school and I was in the early years of my law practice, but we did not become romantically involved until a few years after she graduated and began working at a law firm in Atlanta. From there, our relationship grew quickly. We didn't get engaged until we had dated for a little over two years, but we both knew pretty early on that we would be a permanent thing. I'm going to do my best in this book to avoid trading in too many clichés, but, at least for me, this one was true: when you know, you know.

Looking back, I'm thankful for that initial stage when we got to know each other on a friendship level before we started dating. It allowed us to establish a genuine trust and comfort with each other that can be harder to come by when you date someone before really getting to know them.

Having this foundation of friendship was especially key for us, because I don't think anyone back then would have pegged us as a match. We came from vastly different backgrounds. I grew up in North Miami, Florida—about as far away from Liz's Newnan upbringing as you could get—and Jewish, to boot. Liz had zero Jewish friends in high school and very few in college. Seemingly, we were from different planets.

But thank God we saw past the surface stuff. Although I don't think of myself as an overly sentimental person, I am a spiritual one, and now—having been with Liz for over 15 years—I am convinced that something deeper than the rigors of everyday life connects us. Something spiritual. Something beyond. I truly believe that. We truly believe that.

One of the most important things being with Liz has taught me is the importance of being open to the unexpected and being willing to veer off script, whether the script is yours or one someone else tries to impose on you. Because, like I said, no one who knew us before we coupled up would have ever put us together. But it didn't take us long to realize the special magic of what we'd found in each other. Our spiritual yearning and curiosities. A value system focused on family. And our real North Star: a shared wanderlust. We knew we were meant to explore all of life's wonders together.

A little more on the travel bit. Early in our relationship, we were on a date and scratched out on a restaurant napkin a long list of places we dreamed of visiting together. There wasn't any pre-meditation behind it; we just got excited while talking about all the places we wanted to see and decided it would be fun to write it all down. So we did, while we ate and drank and enjoyed the earliest stages of mapping out our future adventures together.

At the end of our date, Liz tucked this napkin into her purse, and we have gone back to it again and again, scratching off places we've seen while adding others. There's a lot of life recorded on that napkin. It's funny how a crumpled old piece of tissue, created so spontaneously, could take on such profound meaning.

I know I have to go back to July 2, 2019, but it is impossible to capture our full story without touching on her inner strength. It is otherworldly. It takes a steely determination to slog through the twenty-six-point-two miles of a marathon and do all the other endurance stuff she does, and Liz has that attribute in abundance. Time and again when faced with adversity in her life, a red-hot fire inside her ignites. You can literally see it happening, like in a super-hero movie. She has this adorable little vein on her forehead that pops outs in these moments, and I joke with her that when that vein appears I know it's time for me to duck and cover. Because her next words are invariably an ominous warning: "I'm about to go Newnan on you."

I love this about her, too.

True story: one time years ago, while taking a lunch break at work, Liz witnessed a woman getting mugged by three teens and immediately gave chase. No thought, just instinct and the immediate, burning urge to make the situation right. Lucky for the teens, they had a head start and managed to escape. The victim, who was bloodied during the encounter, later thanked Liz but also said, "I'm not sure I would have done that."

No kidding.

I later asked Liz, "What were you going to do if you actually caught them?"

Her response: "I have no idea. I just started running."

There are countless other everyday examples of this. In the game of life, Liz is the one who gives maximum hustle on every play and dives for every loose ball. In many ways, she's a first responder. And while she may not win every battle—she'd be the first to admit it—on those infrequent occasions when she comes up short she's going down throwing uppercuts and haymakers. There is no surrender. It's the only way she knows how to live.

She is, in a word, a force. And while she may not have realized it when she woke up on the morning of July 2, 2019, she was going to need every bit of that strength and determination to survive the gauntlet ahead.

Chapter 3
The Warning Signs

WHILE THE LIGHTNING BOLT struck us on July 2, 2019, there had been some prior warning signs that things were not entirely right. In 2016, shortly after our second child Isaac was born, Liz suffered a minor tear in her abdomen. It was bothersome, but with the time pressures of work and the hands-on demands of raising two young kids, getting a small-ish hernia repaired was not a huge priority for her. So she dealt with it.

By the Spring of 2019, however, Liz decided it was finally time to get this thing taken care of. We vetted a couple surgeons and scheduled surgery for early July.

But during the weeks leading up to Liz's surgery, we started feeling uneasy. While the hernia had been a nuisance for a couple of years, by March 2019, it was causing much more pronounced discomfort. Liz was experiencing a constant sensation of fullness—uncomfortably so—no matter how little or carefully she ate.

Also, the visual evidence of her hernia—previously only a slight protrusion—had grown drastically. And quickly, too. She went from appearing normal to having a noticeable bulge in a couple months. People started asking her when she was expecting (I mean, seriously?!), which made her worried and self-conscious.

There was also an unexplained dip in her energy levels. It wasn't a drastic shift; even at only 75%, Liz was still waking up at 5 AM to get in her morning workout. From the outside looking in, it probably seemed like we were still running at our usual pace, doing the work/family/extra-curricular juggling act that so many working families do. But that extra gear Liz could tap into when she needed it? Now missing. She was showing unfamiliar signs of fatigue.

One moment sticks out. There was a weekend in May when Liz's mother came up from Newnan to babysit the boys for a night so Liz and I could have a full afternoon and evening sans children. Like many parents with young kids, we treasured these opportunities for mini-vacations. We booked a room in a slick new local hotel with a beautiful rooftop pool. The location was killer, just a short walk from shopping and bars with live music and other interesting stuff. We planned to shop, grab lunch, and then hang out by the pool before enjoying dinner at a popular new steak restaurant, followed by a night on the town.

We ended up getting to our hotel pretty early, so we had an early lunch and then headed straight to the pool. We grabbed a couple drinks and set up camp on a large two-person outdoor sofa in the shade. The weather was perfect, and we had the entire afternoon and evening ahead of us. I figured we'd talk and laugh and have all of those rejuvenating conversations that aren't so easy to come by in the day-to-day scramble of our busy lives and with the boys always around.

But when we sat down, Liz took onc sip of her drink, placed it on the side table, snuggled up next to me, and abruptly passed out.

This wasn't the kind of light doze where you drift in and out of semi-consciousness while relaxing and enjoying the warm late-Spring breeze. No, this was a sudden, hard crash that knocked her out for over an hour. It hadn't been a strenuous day—certainly not by her usual standards—but she was absolutely spent. As I sat there rubbing the back of her head, surprised by how deeply she was sleeping through all the splashing and music around us, I had the distinct thought: *something isn't right.*

I said nothing about my unease at the time, but looking back, I realize that was the moment my sixth sense kicked in. Between Liz's discomfort, her digestive distress, the distention in her tummy, and her subdued energy levels, this feeling of *not-quite-right* hung with me over the next several weeks.

So, a few weeks before Liz's scheduled hernia surgery, while our boys were safely asleep in their beds, I suggested Liz go see our family doctor to ensure there weren't any other problems lurking in her abdomen. Liz said she had been thinking exactly the same thing and that she would make an appointment, just to be safe.

That short moment saved Elizabeth's life.

***

Our family doctor is a top-notch sports medicine specialist who we both trusted and had been seeing for years. He ordered blood work and an X-ray of Liz's abdomen, but everything came back normal. This left him unsure what to make of Liz's symptoms, but to his great credit, he encouraged her to keep digging for answers. He suggested two appointments: the first with a gastroenterologist and the second with her gynecologist. Somehow Liz booked both appointments on short notice instead of the "we'll see you in six weeks" routine all too common with medical appointments these days. Another of the many lucky little breaks we are now thankful for in hindsight.

The appointment with the gastroenterologist was unproductive and left Liz frustrated. After the most cursory of examinations, which included no additional bloodwork or other meaningful scrutiny, Liz was told her discomfort was "probably" diet related and that she should moderate her intake of beans and broccoli. And then she was sent on her way without even scheduling a follow-up, much less a referral to another doctor who might investigate her puzzling symptoms a bit more closely. A waste of time and a dead end.

The trip to the gynecologist was a different story. Liz was given a thorough and proper examination. The visit yielded more questions than answers, but was an important step nonetheless. Liz was told her reproductive functioning looked normal and healthy, but something else had caught the attentive eye of a Physician Assistant during a sonogram. An unusual amount of fluid had build-up in her abdomen. The Physician Assistant couldn't say what it was or where it was coming from, but insisted we not ignore it.

The first real alarm bell sounded.

For lack of a better idea, the gynecologist made Liz an appointment with a general surgeon at a major local hospital (which hospital shall remain nameless for a multitude of reasons I choose not to get into). The referral perplexed us. You rarely think about meeting with a surgeon until you first have an underlying diagnosis. But—and this was yet another lucky break we didn't fully appreciate at the time—Liz was able to book an appointment with the surgeon almost immediately.

The surgeon, however, was just as perplexed by the short-notice referral as we were, and he failed spectacularly at hiding his annoyance. As frustrated as Liz had been after her visit with the gastroenterologist, this visit was far worse. This guy wasn't merely careless or dismissive. He was rude and condescending. He told Liz the report of fluid in her abdomen was nothing of concern, simply symptoms of her menstrual cycle or the hernia she was scheduled to have repaired. Nothing to see here.

But since the whole point of heading down this path was to rule out problems other than the hernia itself, Liz pressed for other explanations. The surgeon resisted. He was "ninety-five percent" certain it was the hernia or her cycle. They went around and around, Liz trying to explain the hernia had been an issue for years and the sudden emergence of these incongruous symptoms seemed like something more. The surgeon's refusal to offer a single other *possible* explanation tormented her.

Finally, the gloves came off. Liz demanded we turn the ninety-five percent into one hundred, to ensure that when she went in for her hernia surgery, the doctor wouldn't find some horrible surprise. The surgeon finally, begrudgingly relented, and scheduled Liz for a full MRI. If there was anything else going on inside her, the MRI would let us know.

And so, just a few days before the Broitman family arrived for our weekend at the cabin together, Liz went in for her MRI.

Chapter 4
Appendiceal Adenocarcinoma

BACK TO MID-MORNING, JULY 2, 2019.

I've left my office, raced across town, navigated a giant maze of a parking deck, found Liz, and am sitting with her in a tiny, stark white office.

The oncologist walked in. He was... *young*. Like, improbably young. And the look on his face did not instill hope or confidence. He looked overwhelmed by the moment. He looked frightened.

As Liz and I huddled together on the examination table, box of tissues in hand, this young doctor explained that Liz's MRI revealed a very rare form of appendix cancer—as in less than 1,500 reported cases a year—that would need to be treated, and quickly. Because while appendiceal adenocarcinoma is called "appendix cancer" for short, that description is dangerously misleading. While the disease may start in your appendix, if not contained quickly enough, it will spill out into your abdominal cavity via a mucin-like fluid—hence the distention in Liz's belly—and cover everything within reach like a splattering of paint, causing cancerous tumors to take root anywhere and everywhere. Liz would need surgery right away, we were told, and would likely face long-lasting, possibly permanent changes to her insides and digestive functioning.

Quite the change from the "everything is fine" prognosis we had heard from the same hospital only a few days earlier.

I felt a stress headache coming on from the whiplash. We asked the oncologist to back up and slow down. But he launched right back into all kinds of technical terminology about Liz's mucin and bluntly outlined a barbaric-sounding surgical procedure he would perform to remove the mucin and extinguish all traces of it. We understood little of what he was saying, but the severity of the predicament came through loud and clear.

But the strangest thing about that moment was my fixation on the doctor's age. Forget trying to understand the medical ramifications of what the guy was saying. I was having a hard time even focusing on the words coming out of his mouth. Because when I looked at him, all I could do was gaze in amazement at his boyish face. I was one hundred percent certain he was younger than I, and I was almost as certain he was younger than Liz, too. How could a guy this young be ready for something like this?

When he finally stopped talking for a moment about mucin and carcinomas and asked us if we had any questions, the first thing I blurted out was, "So will you be pledging a fraternity in the upcoming fall semester?" I kid you not. I heard a very faint chortle come from my dear wife sitting beside me.

It was a rotten and out-of-character thing for me to say. I felt bad, but it just didn't seem possible that this twelve-plus hour surgical procedure—which would end with him literally pouring heated chemotherapy into Liz's insides—was going to be performed by a guy who could pass for an underclassman.

The young doctor was unamused by my question, but he maintained composure and carried on. I still think about that exchange with a tinge of regret. It is one of the few times in my life I can honestly remember being so deliberately shitty and not apologizing immediately afterwards. My only excuse? Reality had been suspended. We were in a bad dream.

And we were just getting started.

***

Even now, there is still a part of us that cannot fully process how any of this happened. That disconnect—knowing objectively that something awful had happened, but never quite believing it in your heart—will probably always be with us on some level. I don't say this hyperbolically or in a loose, conversational sense. Trying to make sense of the unexplainable has been an enduring struggle for us (a topic I'll come back to).

The first few weeks after Liz's diagnosis were a total fog. Liz had been a model of picture-perfect health. One minute we had our whole lives ahead of us, and the next we were facing an existential crisis. And this from a threat we had never heard of and couldn't pronounce. We were frightened, disoriented, and in out-of-body disbelief. All the hallmarks of sudden shock, I suppose.

Sleep, as you might imagine, was in short supply. Even if we managed to doze off for a short spell at night after the boys were down, it was fitful. But the worst part was waking up and facing the terror all over again. Every morning there were these precious few seconds when we would forget, just for an instant, what we were facing. But then you'd flick on the bathroom light, or hear your sweet old dog shake her collar, and your semi-conscious brain would power on to full awareness... and boom. The realization would slam into you all over again with a violent, sickening impact. The first fully conscious thought of your day, *every* day, would be: "Oh my God. This is really happening. How could this be happening? This is really our life."

The entire month of July 2019, I dreaded waking up.

***

Things got worse before they got better.

Among the roughly 1,500 annual cases of Liz's disease per year, ninety percent of them are considered "low grade" cancer, meaning the mucin is sedate, slow-moving, and not particularly interested in fighting its way into the vital surrounding organs. It's serious business for sure, but one that has encouraging outcomes with a little luck and quality treatment.

The relatively hopeful prognosis for low grade appendiceal cancer lies in stark contrast to that for high grade, which is far more dangerous because of how aggressively it spreads. Based on feedback we received from multiple medical professionals and from hours of poring over medical literature online, only five to fifteen percent of patients survive more than five years after being diagnosed. The more I dug into the research, the worse it all looked. I finally pulled myself away from all the reports and studies, for fear of driving myself into despair over the hypothetical "what ifs." I couldn't let my mind go there.

Instead, we just kept telling ourselves there was almost no chance she had the high grade. There were a miniscule number of appendiceal cancer patients to begin with, and if only ten percent of that exceedingly low number had the high grade, then statistics were on our side. It calculates to about a one in a billion chance of someone having the high grade. Mathematically, we could win the Powerball jackpot three times—odds: one in 292 million—and still be in the clear.

So, as we got up to speed on the disease, we took baby steps toward compartmentalizing our anxiety. Certainly, no one enjoys hearing they have cancer, but as the unknowns crystallized into knowns, it felt like our situation could be maybe-kinda-sorta not as bad as initially feared. We'd probably face some quality of life issues with the low grade, particularly with the impact on Liz's digestive functioning post-surgery, but we liked our odds of getting through it. The survival rates with the low grade were not horrible, and especially so for someone like Liz, who was young and otherwise in excellent health. Alright, then. We got this!

The biopsy would provide confirmation. We were actually looking forward to it, because the clarity would erase the anxiety. And assuming we were dealing with the low grade cancer—which was statistically far more likely—the surgery would be the end of it. There would be a low risk of the cancer compromising any of her vital organs or returning post-surgery, and we'd be able to return to a semi-normal life. Not even two weeks since the initial diagnosis, we went into the biopsy fully expecting our first bit of good news since July 2.

A few days after the biopsy, I got the second phone call from Liz. Again, while I was at work. The test results had come back. We'd been hit by lightning twice. We had the high grade.

Chapter 5
The High Grade

LOOKING BACK, IT'S DIFFICULT to pinpoint the proverbial "worst" moment of our journey. Obviously there was that first phone call on July 2, but abject shock and disorientation, while frightfully unpleasant, aren't the most emotionally haunting.

Certainly there were many anguishing moments that came later. Liz fully conscious during painful, invasive procedures. Liz on a ventilator post-surgery, tortured for hours by the sensation of suffocation. Liz vibrating with raw pain for weeks on end as her body struggled to recover from it all. All of those horrible moments tested our limits.

But if forced to pick the single worst moment of our journey, the moment we shared when I finally made it home after learning Liz had the high grade would have to be it. That was, to me—and I think to Liz as well—the absolute worst. Our darkest moment.

After sprinting out of my office and racing home, I found Liz pacing back and forth on our front porch. She was frantic. Even her eyes were trembling.

We went inside and into our bedroom. We closed the door behind us and embraced. Her body was a furnace, her heart blasting heat from her chest into mine. I have no idea how long we stood there. Time passed, because that's what time does. Neither of us wanted to let go.

We finally released our long embrace, and that was when everything... broke. The big tears erupted, thunderous and gasping. The violence startled me. Sure, we had shed plenty of tears together over the past few weeks, but this was different. This wasn't merely fear or sadness. This was panic, unmoored and untamed.

Liz shouted defiantly, her words half-enunciated, and then her fists flew. Wild swings through the air, and then down, pummeling the large decorative pillows on our bed. More shouting. Her panic gave way to rage, and rage burned itself into despair. *This is not happening!*

While trying to console Liz, I quickly scanned the room for my phone, wanting to be prepared to call for emergency aid in case this fit escalated into something unable to be contained. I felt sickened and, worse, helpless.

I fought to stay calm and comforting, but inside I was having an adrenaline overload. Panic of my own bubbled toward the surface. Because this felt like the knock-out blow. I can't say we were in great shape before the high grade call, but we had convinced ourselves the news would be low grade, and our belief was enough to maintain our hope. If anyone could slug her way through low grade cancer, it was Liz.

But then... the worst of the "what ifs" barged in and demolished whatever fragile sense of comfort we had constructed for ourselves, a tsunami through a sandcastle. All the plans we had lovingly curated over the past thirteen years—of building a family, of raising our boys, and of taking the adventures we had scratched out on that rumpled napkin together—all of them seemed to disintegrate in that moment.

Because there was—and is—no way to find comfort with the high grade. The surgeries are high risk and brutal. The patients who even make it that far usually end up with poor outcomes and drastically shortened lives. And for those few who make it through the surgeries with positive outcomes, the risk of the cancer returning is alarmingly high. Making it five years is a win. Only a small percentage of patients go on to live their full lives.

We had convinced ourselves we wouldn't have to walk the high grade path, and yet there we were. Liz sobbed and cursed and convulsed, while I was introduced to the exquisite agony of powerlessness. Neither of us could say it, but we both felt it: *This wasn't a fight we were likely to win.*

When Liz's fists stopped swinging, she crumpled on the foot of our bed and buried her face in her hands.

Never before had I felt so utterly, desperately lost.

There was nothing else to do but prop her up, wrap my arms around her, and whisper the only thing I could think to say, over and over: "*I got you, Liz. I got you. I got you.*"

Chapter 6
Mapping Out a Treatment Plan

THAT SUMMER, WE WERE basically in survival mode. It was all about one-foot-in-front-of-the-other and making it to the next day, and the next day, and the next.

But at the same time, we had to decide on a course for Liz's treatment. While I am not proud of the way I spoke to the young doctor at the hospital where Liz was diagnosed, Liz and I had agreed after that visit I wasn't wrong to wonder if this was the right medical team for us. Youthful appearance aside, there was a serious question of experience. One of the few semi-coherent questions we asked during our visit with this doctor was whether he had ever served as lead surgeon on the type of surgery Liz would be facing. He had not. And while he had a top-notch academic pedigree, we didn't want Liz to be his very first patient on this procedure.

We began making phone calls and doing our diligence. The early feedback confirmed our instincts: experience matters. The rarer the disease, the more imperative it is to find an expert in the field. While Unnamed Hospital has a fine reputation, our margin for error was razor-thin and we were unwilling to take any chances. We decided we would go wherever we needed to get the best treatment available, even if it meant pulling our boys out of their schools and relocating our family.

We put out feelers everywhere, and while a few led to dead-ends—not unexpected, given the rarity of the disease—two unrelated sources came back with the same recommendation: Dr. Charles Staley at Emory Cancer Winship Center. Both sources said he was an expert in the field, that he performed a high number of these surgeries per year (which was surprising, given how few of these surgeries get performed), and that he had an impeccable reputation both at Emory and with other cancer treatment hospitals.

We left him a voicemail late on a Friday afternoon, and he called us back almost immediately and cleared an opening to see Liz that following Monday. He reviewed Liz's scans over the weekend and had detailed treatment plans for Liz when we arrived, which he explained to us in plain English. He was empathetic and patient as we fumbled our way through our long list of questions. He addressed the risks facing us in a calm, comforting way that made us feel as reassured as we could under the circumstances. He somehow even injected a little humor into the meeting. "You just need a tune-up," he said. Somehow, we found ourselves smiling.

There was no doubt about it after that first meeting with Dr. Staley. We had our man.

Our treatment plan with Dr. Staley would consist of six rounds of chemotherapy pre-surgery. Then the surgery itself, to remove all of her tumors and diseased tissue. And then, more than likely, another several rounds of chemo post-surgery as soon as her body healed enough to tolerate the additional treatment. The aim was to leave behind no traces of disease, not even on a microscopic level. The only way to beat the long odds facing us was to get it exactly right the first time.

Besides providing a world-class surgeon, Emory also arranged for Liz to take part in a clinical trial for the type of chemo she would receive. She would be treated on a separate floor in the hospital, in her own nicely appointed infusion room overlooking a picturesque outdoor garden. Liz jokingly referred to the set-up as our "stay at the Ritz Carlton." Having such comfortable accommodations was no small thing. Her infusion sessions were all-day affairs of being pricked and stuck and prodded. Having a little privacy and a comfortable room was a luxury that went a long way.

This clinical trial also required Liz, after her infusions at the hospital, to wear a small pump through the weekends. While we accepted this as a necessary part of the deal, having something literally attached to Liz's body for several days at a time was stressful and dispiriting. Even just the *sound* of it. While barely audible during the business of the day, the somber echo of its motorized whir was all we could hear lying awake at night.

But even worse than its sound, the pump made Liz feel fragile. The plastic tube running from the little black satchel hanging over her shoulder and into the port in her chest was visible proof of her illness for the entire world to see. Liz would sometimes recount to me to horrible sensation of being stared at or—even worse—gazed upon with pity. She told me it was a feeling far worse than any physical discomfort.

Then there was the practical concern of having two small boys who longed for the comfort and affection of their parents. Cuddling was a dicey proposition for Liz because getting the boys tangled up in her pump could cause her serious injury. So Liz did what she could with them in small, delicate measures. "Careful with mommy's pump" became a sad and frequent household refrain.

Liz's chemo pump aside, we did everything we could to keep things as normal as possible for the boys at home until the big day of Liz's surgery. Behind closed doors, Liz and I had the tough conversations about the unexpected turn our life had taken and how we would manage through all the various scenarios, including the unimaginably tragic ones you pray you never have to experience with anyone, much less your spouse (and mother of your two small children).

But we were determined to prevent the storm clouds from blocking out the sun for Eli and Isaac. Best we could, we carried on with summer camps and beach trips and afternoons of junk food and roller coasters at Six Flags. Liz began to half-kiddingly refer to herself as the "Yes Mom," desperate to collect family memories while we could. As hard as it was, we muscled through. The need to protect our children outweighed our fear and exhaustion.

The "C" word was strictly off-limits in their presence. When Eli had occasional questions about mommy (Isaac was too young to have any sense of what was going on), we spoke to him in careful, optimistic terms. We didn't want to outright lie to him, of course, but we also didn't want to give him cause to worry, either. It was a delicate balance.

Little kids are scary perceptive, though. And they can sense when things aren't right, even if they can't put a finger on it or articulate why. Looking back, it's hard to say what was connecting with Eli and what wasn't, but he clearly knew something was up.

One memory stands out. In mid-August—so about six weeks after the diagnosis and a little less than a month after Liz started chemo—we took a quick family beach trip down to Florida. We still had a few months before Liz's surgery and we wanted to make the most of that time. One afternoon, we camped out by the pool. Liz and Isaac decided to take a snooze under an umbrella while Eli and I bounded back and forth from pool to hot tub. We'd spend a few minutes in one and then it would be back to the other. He found this great fun.

During one of these back-and-forths, we came back from the pool to find a young mother and her kids plopped in the hot tub. This was exciting news for Eli, who never misses an opportunity to start up conversations with new people. He began chattering away about dinosaurs and trains and Disney movies and all kinds of other random things—he can cover a lot of ground in a hurry—and when he finally stopped to take a breath, the mother chimed in.

"You guys here by yourself?"

"No. I'm here with my brother and my mother, too. She has bad cells."

"I'm sorry—she what?"

"She has bad cells. In her tummy."

The mother opened her mouth to speak and then caught herself. *Oh.*

Three silent seconds that felt like three years as she and I both tried to figure out what to say. Then Eli jumped up.

"Let's go back to the pool, DaDa!"

I got up, offered a quick "nice to meet you," and turned away. Eli was already a few steps ahead of me, headed towards the pool. As I followed him, I could feel the young mother's gaze. I turned back. Our eyes met. It was the expression Liz had learned to dread. It was that look of pity.

Chapter 7

Grinding Through the Summer

We had a dizzying number of appointments from July through the Fall. Of course, there were several visits with Dr. Staley, who was collecting information and gearing up to perform Liz's surgery after we completed her first six rounds of chemo. Also with the oncologist, who selected the precise mixture of chemicals for Liz's chemotherapy treatments, and who needed to keep a close watch on how Liz was dealing with the side-effects. And then there were the six chemo infusions themselves, those all day affairs at our "Ritz Carlton."

In between those appointments were several CT scans, MRIs, and stops at the lab for blood samples. Also, Liz had to get her port put in for the chemo infusions, a minor surgical procedure unto itself. And she needed a colonoscopy. Some days we would finish one appointment, run down to the cafeteria for a quick lunch, and head straight to the next one. The Emory hospital is a pretty big place, but within a couple months we knew the joint inside and out. The parking valets knew us by name.

When not running from appointment to appointment, we were working the phones. We contacted other cancer specialists to get second and third opinions on Liz's scans (yep, still the high grade). We communicated regularly with the Miller Cancer Institute in Miami (one of the sources that led us to Dr. Staley) to keep them informed on the progress of Liz's treatment.

Meanwhile, Liz was reading everything she could get her hands on concerning appendix cancer treatments and outcomes, constantly seeking information that might give us even a glimmer of hope.

On top of all this medical stuff, there was our emotional wellbeing to tend to. We may not have known much about Liz's cancer when we got started, but we knew we had to stay positive to have a fighting chance. We couldn't see ourselves getting through it any other way.

Fortunately, the emphasis on staying hopeful wasn't a big stretch for us. Positivity runs in our DNA. I know my account so far has been dark and difficult, but Liz and I are devout optimists at heart. And spiritual, too, which is a big driver of that optimism. We often remarked that our world had become one in which terror and faith walked hand in hand. So we leaned in hard on the faith part.

While faith and spirituality had always been key parts of our life, fortunately we had been taking them to deeper levels during the year leading up to July 2, 2019. If you believe in that sort of thing, you could almost say we'd been led to prepare.

A few months before Liz's diagnosis, we took part in a terrific weekend retreat with other interfaith couples from our Temple community. We came back from the retreat energized and with lots of great ideas about new religious traditions we wanted to create for our family. So, as soon as Liz was diagnosed, one of our first moves was to reach out to the Rabbi for added prayer and spiritual guidance. It's an investment that pays dividends over and over again. More on this later.

While we each did some of our own self-care work separately—and Part II of this book gets into my piece of it as the caregiver, specifically—we felt it was imperative to stay in emotional lockstep. We participated in joint therapy sessions to process and cope with the strain as a couple. We did joint meditation and breathing sessions. We took long walks together. Anything we could think of to clear our heads, connect, and pay homage to the bond between us, we did. Because we knew that bond would be our armor against every upcoming threat.

***

As Liz's surgery approached, there was one more test that needed to be performed. There's a lot still unknown about Liz's disease ("why can't I just get normal cancer like everyone else?" was Liz's go-to gallows quip) so researchers are exploring genetic testing. The test they wished to run on Liz would determine whether a hereditary genetic mutation caused her cancer. To assess the risk of this being passed down to our boys.

This was my big breakdown moment. None of these appointments were easy, but introducing our boys into the mix? On top of everything else Liz was going through? While it was common for us both to shed a tear or two during Liz's medical appointments, those moments usually passed pretty quickly. We'd recompose and get ourselves back on track. But not this time. This time, I fell apart. Much like the day I tried to console Liz when we learned she had the high-grade, only now with roles reversed. Liz wrapped her arms around me while the doctor waited. Patiently, I should add.

But it started again when I went back to work that afternoon. I couldn't think about anything else while those lab results were pending. The uncertainties and the horrible what ifs—certainly with Liz, and now too with the boys—were devouring me. I got to my office, closed my door, and hid under my desk.

The results from the genetics test took only a few days, but it seemed like an eternity. The test came back favorable—finally some good news—but my mind had gone to some really dark places. I knew then I had to seek professional help to manage my grief. The weight was threatening to become too great to carry. Whatever happened to Liz, the boys were going to need me to be in the best possible headspace to carry us through it. This decision to seek professional help was one of the most important decisions I made during that time.

***

So a little more about the work situation during this early stage. Liz went on disability the day we got her diagnosis, but I still had a law practice to maintain. The first few weeks after Liz's diagnosis, balancing work with all the medical appointments was especially difficult because we had decided to keep our situation under wraps until we had a handle on what we were facing. We shared the news only with family and our innermost circle of friends.

Once we understood the treatment plan, though, we knew we would need to tell people sooner rather than later. There would be no hiding it once she started walking around with a chemotherapy pump. We decided I had to inform my law partners first, so my constant disappearances from the office wouldn't alarm them. If you've ever wondered what a lawyer-in-distress-breaking-bad-news-to-his-law-partners-email looks like (and honestly, who hasn't?), it goes something like this:

July 20, 2019

All,

Hope you are having a good weekend. Apologies for using email to communicate news of this nature, but am writing to share some things that are going on with my family that aren't super fun to talk about in person.

For the past several months, Liz has been dealing with substantial bloating and abdominal discomfort. After meeting with a number of doctors (and after a few really bad misses by some of the docs we saw), we learned she has a rare cancer known as appendiceal adenocarcinoma (aka high grade appendix cancer). We've spent most of the month of July trying to wrap our brains around what this means for us and our boys.

Certainly, we're not happy about this and I'm not going and tell you there haven't been awful moments and several sleepiness nights. But the good news is, notwithstanding the rarity of this disease, there is a national specialist at Emory who is treating us and who has us on a plan. Liz starts chemo next week and will have surgery to remove all the tumors and cancerous tissue in her abdomen in a couple of months. Liz is as tough and determined as they come, so we are unshaken in our belief that she will have a full and healthy recovery. Also, we've had a tremendous amount of support from our families, close friends, and Temple (nobody does comfort food better than the Jews) for which we are eternally thankful.

My plan is to work and be as productive as I can during these next several months, but obviously I'm going to be spending a substantial amount of time with Liz in treatments and consultations and recoveries and the like. I'll keep you posted as things progress and as to my whereabouts. In the meantime, I'm fine if you share this news with the associates in our office if anyone asks, but let's please not make this common knowledge among the staff. I know people are well intentioned and Liz has many friends here, but I really can't be engaging in constant chitchat over this without losing my shit.

Positivity and high fives are what I am looking for, my friends. I'm sure there will be other tough moments, but we absolutely got this. Thank you, a million times over, for your friendship and your support.

Matt

A little background on my law firm. I started there right after law school and it's the only law job I've ever had. Many of us have been there for over twenty years together, including my legal assistant, the receptionist, the office manager, and several of my law partners. They are very much part of my Atlanta family, and that familial relationship has been far and away the best part of the gig. So it is not at all surprising that within moments of sending this email, I received a flood of responses overflowing with love and encouragement and support. *Take care of your family*, I was told. *We got you.*

And they did. It's difficult to disentangle yourself from cases that have been pending for years, and I still had to earn a living. The world doesn't stop just because you are facing a challenge. But the reinforcements arrived with gusto. Where it was feasible, my cases got staffed with additional lawyers to run things while I was away. I stayed involved as much as I could, but they took most of the day-to-day stuff off of my plate. I had breathing room.

Plus, everyone was really cool about following my lead in terms of the emotional fallout. They respected the boundaries I requested, but they also would instantly drop things when I felt the tension ratcheting up and needed to vent.

This email released a humongous pressure valve. I frankly don't know how we would have made it through without my Atlanta family. I'm unspeakably thankful for their level of grace.

Chapter 8
Bracing for the Main Event

In early November—after all the appointments, the counseling sessions (hers, mine, ours), the genetics testing, and the chemotherapy—we were finally scheduled to go in for what Dr. Staley called, only somewhat jokingly, the MOAS. Shorthand for *Mother of All Surgeries*. During our final meeting with him before the MOAS, he gave us a more detailed understanding of what to expect in terms of the procedure and its risks.

The MOAS would consist of two parts. First, they would open up Liz's abdomen to locate and remove all the diseased tissue. The high-grade mucin often causes cancerous "barnacles" to attach to whatever internal organ it contacts, so those barnacles would need to be removed, along with all the mucinous fluid itself, of course. Hopefully, any barnacles that Dr. Staley found would be latched only to the outer shells of Liz's organs. In that event, Dr. Staley could just scrape them off and move to the second part of the surgery: the HIPEC.

HIPEC stands for *hyperthermic intraperitoneal chemotherapy*. In plain English, highly concentrated chemotherapy is heated to 105 degrees and poured into Liz's abdomen. And then, as crazy as this sounds, the surgical team physically rocks the operating table back and forth, with Liz still on it, to swish the heated mix of chemicals around her inner nooks and crannies for ninety minutes. Understand something: normal human cells die at 110 degrees. So they would also need to cover her with ice during this HIPEC treatment to prevent her from being cooked alive.

The goal is to ensure no cancerous cells remain. Not even on a microscopic level.

What I'm describing is the best-case scenario. The tougher scenario would be if the barnacles had not just latched to the outer shell of Liz's organs, but had penetrated inside the organs themselves. Removing *those* barnacles was a far more difficult and dangerous task.

For any non-vital organs (gall bladder, spleen) that were breached, the call was easy: you remove the organ. We actually already expected those organs would need to be removed during her procedure, anyway. Also, because of its proximity to Liz's now-ruptured appendix, we knew that some to-be-determined portion of her large intestine would need to be removed as well. Liz's digestive functioning was going to be permanently impacted in some way. We knew this going in.

The wild cards were Liz's liver, kidneys, and especially her small intestines. As we understood it, whether and to what extent Liz's cancer had penetrated these organs would greatly impact both the risks of the surgery itself and also Liz's long-term health prospects.

The worst-case scenario—and Dr. Staley was as gentle and tactful as he could be about this—was the one where the doctor opens you up, surveys the landscape, and determines there is nothing to be done.

But assuming we weren't facing that worst-case scenario, Dr. Staley would meticulously extract every bit of diseased tissue he could find and send us home to live the rest of our lives. There would be other judgment calls to make. For example, how much damage to her ovaries must there be before you decide to remove them instead of trying to save them? But for us, these decisions weren't tough at all. We told the good doctor to err on the side of caution and remove anything and everything if it meant reducing the risk of the cancer returning. Even if it meant a tougher recovery, "*Just get her home alive*" was our response to every "what if" question we faced.

Dr. Staley assured us that was exactly what he intended to do, but he didn't sugarcoat it. He would be taking her to the verge of death and then bringing her back. And it didn't sound like hyperbole when he said it.

Going into the surgery with so many unknowns is one of the most pernicious things about this disease. There was no way to know the full picture until Dr. Staley got inside. Even with modern technology, there are limitations to what the scans and bloodwork could tell us about the high-grade mucin and cancerous barnacles. We would have to wait and see if the walls protecting Liz's vital organs had been breached.

There was simply no way to know until we knew.

***

Shortly before Liz's surgery, my dad and step-mother came up from Florida to stay with us for a weekend. We were trying to keep things as normal as possible, and so we did what we usually do during their visits. Namely, take the boys to and from their various activities and otherwise lounge around the house.

The first day was all small talk. The six-ton elephant in the room went unaddressed.

On the second night, the group decided on pizza for dinner, so Dad and I ran up the street to pick it up. This was another ritual of ours. Whenever Dad came to town and the family decided on takeout, he and I would leave early for the pickup so we could enjoy a quiet moment together over a drink at the bar. I liked this ritual a lot. Usually, this would be the only time we had alone over the weekend.

Typically, there'd be no shortage of things for us to talk about. Politics, work, Liz and the boys... you name it. With Dad, conversation flows free and easy. Sometimes we'd even order a second round, even if the food was ready, just so we could keep it going for another few minutes. But this time, waiting for the pizza, sipping our beers, no words came. Silence.

My mind churned. I desperately wanted to say something to my dad, but it was too painful to get the words out.

Finally, right as they were boxing up our order, I cleared my throat.

"Listen, Dad. I just want you to know something."

He went still. I cleared my throat again.

"I know you know this is serious. We're doing a lot of praying and staying positive, and we know we're in great hands with Dr. Staley. But we don't have any concrete assurances about how this is going to go. It all depends on what he sees when he gets in there."

"Matt—"

"No, Dad... it's OK. I have to face this and I have to say this. I've spent a lot of time talking to my therapist, and no matter what happens, I have to be able to say this out loud. Because not being able to say it makes it worse."

He nodded at me to continue.

"No matter what happens, I am going to be ok. And the boys will be ok. They deserve a normal, happy childhood that isn't weighed down by tragedy, and I am going to give that to them. No matter what. *No matter what*. We'll figure it out. I'm scared and I'm heartsick, but I can do this."

Dad's eyes welled up. He told me he loved me. He embraced me for a long time. Then we finished the last of our beers and headed home.

Chapter 9
The Surgery and the Aftermath

AFTER OUR FINAL MEETING with Dr. Staley, there were a bunch of meetings with hospital administrators and nursing staff. A surgery of this magnitude requires meticulous preparation at every level.

They gave us all kinds of things to read, and a few days before the surgery we had an hour-long appointment with a physician's assistant who gave us detailed instructions on how to ready ourselves for the big event. We covered everything from the type of soap Liz should use—and how best to gently scrub herself the morning of her surgery—to where we should park when arriving at the hospital. No detail was too small.

They also gave us a strange handheld plastic device. It was rectangular, with a mouthpiece on one end and a little measuring bobber on the other. The little bobber went up and down when you breathed into the mouthpiece. Although it looked like a kid's musical instrument, it was actually a piece of exercise equipment. For her lungs. It also precisely measured her breathing capacity.

Because the surgery would severely weaken her lungs, this little apparatus would be necessary to bring her breathing back to normal.

You know you're bracing for something rough when they somberly explain to you the importance of doing your lung exercises once you're off the ventilator. Followed by a reminder to be sure to bring your medical directive and living will.

***

Shortly before bedtime the night before the surgery, Liz presented the boys and me with separately wrapped going-away gifts. She gave us each our own dreamcatcher—a gift Native American mothers would give their children when they needed to be away from the village for an extended period. Liz told the boys she would be gone for a few weeks, but she loved them and would watch over them.

She also wrote a note for Dr. Staley. She thanked him for everything he had done for her, told him she was praying for him, and asked him to please return her safely to her family.

***

November 6, 2019.

That morning, we were actually pretty upbeat. We had done everything we could and were surrendering Liz's well-being to the care of Emory and Dr. Staley. There is a strange yet certain peace to just letting go and leaning on your faith.

I could see Liz suppressing a smile as we got in the car. The doors closed, and she told me she had a special song for the occasion. Before I could guess, a familiar high-pitched organ blasted from the speakers and transported me back to the era of first generation MTV videos and ubiquitous parachute pants:

Dearly beloved...
We are gathered here today to get through this thing called "life"
Electric word, life
It means forever and that's a mighty long time
But I'm here to tell you, there's something else
The afterworld

Yep. She went there.

So here we are, hours away from sunrise, marching into this most consequential of moments, and she's selected Prince's *Let's Go Crazy* for our entrance song. At that point, all you can do is jump in and sing along as loud as you can—vocal chords be damned.

We're all excited
Don't know why

Maybe its 'cause
We're all gonna die
When we do
What's it all for?
Better live now
Before the grim reaper comes knocking on your door

We put on a stellar performance, if I do say so myself. Even with zero rehearsals beforehand and driving to Emory in total darkness, we nailed the harmonies and kicked righteous ass on all the air guitar solos. *Let's Go Crazy*, indeed.

***

A quick sidebar. It's important to note that I have Liz's full blessing to tell our story in an open and authentic way from my vantage point—warts, tears, and all. I wouldn't have dreamed of starting a project like this without her absolute OK.

Of course, Liz has her own unique perspective—one that she has written and spoken about extensively. She has, deservedly, become a well-known figure within certain circles and a beacon of hope for other patients of rare cancers and other diseases. Our story, ultimately, is a story about Liz, her spirit, and her endurance.

But the caregiver's perspective is a different take, and Liz was adamant my voice not be filtered through her prism. I'm a heart-on-my-sleeve kind of guy anyway, so I wouldn't know how to approach the telling of our story (and the ensuing lessons I have learned) any differently. Still, I'm eternally thankful for Liz's support, because it would be understandably easy for someone in Liz's shoes to lose sight of the fact that cancer's ripples carry to all shores. The caregiver faces uniquely stressful challenges, as I now well know, and she believes there is value in sharing that perspective. All to say I had full license from Liz to share or not share as I saw fit. She wanted me to tell *my* story.

Even so, some moments of this story are best left to just Liz and me.

Like the few private moments we shared in the pre-op waiting area before they wheeled her into the operating room. Getting into those intimate details wouldn't serve the purpose of this book, and, frankly, whatever you imagine those moments were like probably isn't too far off. It's in your gut, right? Besides, there are no words to adequately capture everything we were feeling as we leapt into the unknown.

What I will share is that by the time they wheeled Liz into the OR and escorted me out to the waiting area, the waiting room was crammed. Our parents and step-parents. Our siblings. Liz's aunt.

The Rabbi. Several close friends. I hugged everyone. My adrenaline was at an eleven. We formed our chairs into a large circle. We sat.

And then we waited.

***

Thirteen hours later, my phone rang. I was just outside the hospital, sitting on a park bench to get some fresh nighttime air.

"Dr. Staley is out and ready to see you."

I hustled back inside and found him waiting for me right outside the waiting room. The first thing I remember thinking was: *He looks really tired*. During our previous visits, he was always upbeat and high-energy, but now his usual booming voice was muted. It was clear he'd been through the wringer. I braced myself.

The news was a mixed bag.

The good news was Liz "did well" through the procedure and was out and resting. They would take me to see her shortly. After holding my breath for thirteen hours, I exhaled.

The tougher news was that the disease had been widespread. Dr. Staley didn't mince words here: he told me he removed "buckets" of mucin from her abdomen and the barnacles he'd warned us about were everywhere. No penetration of her small intestine (huge sigh of relief), but they'd made a mess of and attached to just about everything else. They'd had to summon a liver specialist into action midway through the procedure. She'd needed four blood transfusions to get through it all.

To this day, I find myself saying little prayers of thanks for finding Dr. Staley. No way we'd have made it through the surgery in less capable or less experienced hands.

I thanked Dr. Staley, ran to tell everyone the news, and headed to the ICU.

***

We spent nineteen days in the hospital post-surgery. Save for a handful of barely there laughs or a few one second glimpses of Liz's beautiful smile, those nineteen days were a grinding, joyless ordeal.

Honestly, that time existed in a place beyond what we ever could have been ready for. It's one thing to be told about the magnitude and impact of the procedure itself. We heard Emory and Dr. Staley loud and clear on all the stats and technical jargon. But living in the reverberation of those post-surgery shockwaves is another thing altogether. We knew everything going in, but we also had no idea.

And "shockwaves" is no exaggeration. One of the first things they told me when I got to our room in the ICU was to stay out of the bathroom and use the one up the hall instead. This was to make sure I avoided hazardous exposure to any of the HIPEC chemicals that had been poured into Liz's body. The techs who drew blood or otherwise came in close contact with her wore hazmat suits. For those first few days post-surgery, the shining light of my life was radioactive.

The physical devastation wasn't just from the chemicals. It was everything else they did during the hours of surgery leading up to the HIPEC. We didn't learn all the surgical details right away, but she had 52 heavy staples running from her chest all the way down below her bikini line and a tangled maze of what seemed like hundred of tubes running in and out of her.

Obviously, we were relieved she survived the surgery. That part we understood and did not take for granted. But everything else felt up in the air and disorienting. Trapped in a tiny room, overwhelmed by beeping monitors and squawking equipment. A revolving door of doctors and nurses treating Liz at all hours. No sleep routine to settle into. Minutes melting into hours and hours blurring into days.

Liz's mother and I began rotating nights with Liz so I could run home, shower, and spend a little time with the boys. While necessary, this back and forth was enormously taxing. It felt like I was always missing from where I was needed. When I was with Liz, I was worried about the boys. And when I was with the boys, I was worried about Liz.

One evening, I came home to spend the night with the boys and I absentmindedly silenced my phone. Around midnight, I was awakened by heavy pounding on the front door. I jumped out of bed. *What the...?*

Opening that door is another of those frozen-in-time moments I'll always carry with me. There stood Liz's best friend, Lauren, wearing the look of someone sent to deliver terrible news. I'll never, ever forget that look.

I closed my eyes and waited with dread for whatever came next.

Lauren spoke quickly. Liz was alive but her heart rate had suddenly doubled, veering into dangerous territory. The doctors and technicians were scrambling to get it under control. But since my phone was silenced, nobody could reach me.

"Get there safely, but go now. I've got the boys."

I grabbed my keys and sped off to Emory, still in my bedroom slippers.

***

When I arrived, there were so many people in Liz's room I could barely find a place to stand. It was a chaotic scene. A few minutes later, her medical team figured out the issue—apparently, a picc line was the culprit—and Liz's heart rate returned to normal. All fine. But even so, I was furious with myself for being so careless with my phone.

Then it was back to the joyless grind again. Waiting to get Liz back home. And praying there wouldn't be more frightening episodes.

Because of how many hours Liz was under anesthesia during her surgery and because of all the painkillers and other medication she was on afterwards, she was in and out of a coherent state for much of our hospital stay. Ironically, her alert moments were almost worse, because of the anxiety: *What in the world just happened? Will we ever recover from this? Did they get it all? What happens next?*

We realized we hadn't reached the end of our journey. In fact, it felt like another starting line. We didn't know where we were headed, but we knew we had a long way to go.

Chapter 10
Coming Home

When we finally came home, Liz's spirit was broken.

There is no other or more elegant way to say it. As much as she hates being thought of that way, Liz was broken. Turns out, there was nothing hyperbolic about Dr. Staley's promise to take her to the verge of death. She had endured a trauma of the highest order.

During Liz's first return visit to Emory after we had been discharged, we learned the full extent of her procedure. Because of the wider-than-expected spread of the disease, Dr. Staley removed the remnants of her ruptured appendix, her uterus, ovaries, gallbladder, spleen, one of the arteries leading to her stomach, and peritoneum (the membrane lining the cavity of your abdomen that covers your abdominal organs). He also removed half of her large intestine and scraped barnacles off the outer linings of her kidneys, diaphragm, and liver.

The physical toll of the surgery—both in terms of the procedure itself and because of the ensuing days when she could only receive nutrition intravenously—left her emaciated and frail. She'd lost twenty pounds of muscle over three weeks. Even the shape of her face looked different. And her typically bright and electric eyes were glazed and sunken. Only the beautiful smile remained, but that heart-warming reminder of her former self seldom appeared during those first weeks home.

She required ongoing, hands-on care. Everything from help in and out of bed to escorts to the restroom and everything in between. She could barely move her arms from her side. She needed help getting dressed, undressed, and bathed. Plus, the pain was constant and unforgiving. The few steps from our bed to the bathtub and then from the bathtub to the bathroom were slow and labored events.

Getting her adequate nutrition was a big issue too, because her digestive system was wrecked. Back in the hospital, Liz received her sustenance from an IV, broths, and an occasional chocolate pudding as a treat. At home, re-introducing normal eating proved just as difficult as the doctors had warned. Her functioning was spastic and unpredictable, swinging from one extreme of distress to the other with little warning. The unpredictability of how she would feel after eating caused great apprehension and feelings of helplessness.

She was, in every way, a stranger in her own body. The former marathoner, now barely able to navigate the five steps from living room to main floor. The former power lifter, now unable to get in and out of the bathtub without help, much less towel off after. I know she appreciated all the hands-on help, but not being able to do basic things for herself was a misery beyond the physical pain.

She was also flat-out exhausted—often too tired even to hold her phone. Her pain was near constant despite all the medications. Her sleep was uncomfortable and sporadic. Relief was desperately rare.

But as tough as the physical recovery was, the mental recovery was even tougher. Liz's anxiety was off-the-charts, worse than our darkest days of worry before the surgery. Although she had never suffered from claustrophobia before, being bedridden and hooked up to tubes and harnesses and such for so many days had left her unable to even put on a seatbelt without a surge of panic. Sometimes while I was driving her to this place or that, she'd cry out for me to pull over so I could ever-so-delicately unbuckle her seatbelt. The feeling of restraint overwhelmed her. We would idle on the shoulder for several minutes while waiting for her gasps and racing heart to calm.

This panic haunted her into the night. Liz told me about frequent nightmares of losing her life and the devastation it would cause the boys and me. She'd dream that Dr. Staley had missed something, and microscopic cancer cells were already aggressively multiplying inside her. She even tearfully confided to me one night that if her cancer did return, she didn't believe she could endure a second surgery. As long as I've known her, that is the only time I've ever heard Liz doubt whether she was up to facing a challenge.

She would later share with me her worry that she would not survive the recovery. "*This is what it feels like to be dying*," she told herself. I'll confess... I shared that worry. My Superwoman appeared beaten.

But perhaps the hardest thing for her—and the biggest tell for me in terms of how much she was suffering—was her bottomed-out threshold for the boys.

Now don't get me wrong here. She was obviously relieved to be home and thankful the boys had seen her return safely. But during those dark early days, they were far too noisy and rambunctious for Liz to engage with them for more than a few moments at a time. So even though it made me heartsick, I worked hard to keep them occupied and away from her.

In every sense, she was barely hanging on.

***

All of this made for a particularly intense time for me as well. While there have been many stages of this journey for me these past few years, the first several months at home post-surgery were when I served as a caregiver in the most literal sense. Liz needed constant hands-on help, and the ripple-effect of her condition meant I was pulling double-duty on everything else in our lives: the cooking, the cleaning, and—most consequentially—the care for the boys. And that's before accounting for the fact I was still handling an active (albeit reduced) caseload at work. The unrelenting responsibilities of life pulled me in every direction. It felt like a non-stop, all-out sprint. Through a thunderstorm. I was thrashed.

Now, it is important I not understate the amount of help we received: from Liz's mom and sister, from my family, and from an ever-expanding circle of friends. We had a meal train covering most dinners for us, which started months before Liz's surgery and ran well into the Spring of 2020. We also had a live-in nanny helping with day-to-day care for the boys. By no means was I alone. Help was all around. I can't imagine what it would have been like without it.

But even so, the load on my shoulders was daunting. No matter how much help people provided, they all had their own homes and lives to return to. But for me, this *was* home. There was no quiet, normal place to return to for respite or a recharge. I'd go to bed exhausted but unable to sleep, stressed by the knowledge I was facing more of the same the following day. And the next. And the next.

Here's the other thing: although we had plenty of help available, there was only so much responsibility I was prepared to abdicate. Yes, I needed the help, but I also never wanted to be away from home for too long. That was high-priority for me from the very beginning and remained constant. This is why Liz's mom and I traded nights at the hospital. Hard as it was to leave Liz, I wasn't willing to leave the boys for days on end. I couldn't bear the thought of them wondering why Mommy and Daddy both were gone, and when or if they would return.

Because here's the thing about the caregiver role, at least for me. Caregiving isn't just about providing hands-on *care*. More importantly, it's about providing hands-on *comfort.* For Liz, of course, but in some ways even more so for the boys, who were not old enough to grasp what was happening, and who I am sure were feeling like their mother had disappeared on them.

I could already sense trouble bubbling below the surface. Our oldest son, Eli, was showing some worrisome out-of-character behaviors. After Liz had been away at the hospital for a few weeks, his exuberant, happy-go-lucky disposition began to flicker with unpredictable and periodic episodes of uncontrolled rage. On one especially disconcerting occasion, he upended a bookshelf in his room, tore pictures out of picture frames, and smashed his tiny fists into everything within reach. I'd never seen anything like that out of him. These signs of distress told me—notwithstanding all the surrounding help—that I needed to be the stabilizing force.

But I knew I couldn't be that force if I didn't put in the time. So, even with all the focus on Liz, and even with the grind of my work responsibilities, I fought to keep us in our daily routines as much as possible and to stay forefront in their daily lives. I drove Eli to school every morning and handled the evening routine for both boys most nights, too: from bath and teeth brushing to bed and storytelling, sweet dreams and all. If I wasn't at the office or taking Liz to an appointment, I was with the boys. No downtime.

Especially so on the weekends. It would be about a year before Liz had the stamina to fully engage with the boys for long, uninterrupted stretches. During that stretch, Liz would sleep in, spend what time she could manage with the boys, and then take a long nap to recharge. So I was always on call. I'd keep them as busy as I could, with lots of trips to nearby parks and playgrounds and arcades so Liz could get a few quiet hours of rest.

For many, many months, it was just powering through. One foot in front of the other. Praying for Liz's return to strength and health.

***

Looking back on this stage of our journey conjures up mixed feelings for me. On the one hand, those trying times took me through a vast range of grief and anxiety I am still working through.

On the other hand, my heart believes those times also deeply strengthened the bond among Team Ames. Liz and I have a theory that going through a major crisis either divides a family or brings them closer together. For us—in a big, big way—it was the latter. I can't help but be thankful for that.

And on a more personal level, sometimes navigating your way through a crisis provides an opportunity to learn a few things about yourself. There's a lot I didn't get figured out during that first year post-surgery—and to be clear, learning is a lifelong process if you're doing it right. But as I share in Part II, even as your heart aches, it can lead you to some pretty amazing realizations. You just have to be able to endure the pain.

When you're walking in the dark, you can end up covering more ground than you realize.

Chapter 11
Released Into the Wild

WHILE LIZ RECOVERED AT home, her doctors had a judgment call to make regarding her treatment. She needed six more rounds of chemotherapy, urgently, but there was no way her body could endure that in her weakened state. Waiting until she was "fully recovered" (no such thing) wasn't viable, either, so the delicate balancing act was to wait until she was barely strong enough to get through it.

These were agonizing discussions. Here she was—exhausted, beaten, frail—now assigned with the near-impossible task of helping the doctors discern when she'd be ready to feel even worse. I understand why her input mattered from a clinical perspective, but it was a heavy ask emotionally.

I found myself fighting feelings of resentment. While none of this was Emory's fault, I couldn't help but wonder how much earlier we might have caught Liz's disease if some of the providers she'd first met with had paid a little closer attention to what she was telling them about her symptoms. So only *now*—after everything she's been put through—is everyone hanging on her every word and wanting to know precisely what she's feeling? I still get hot looking back on all this.

But as much as we hated it, we knew there was no other way. So we talked at length about how Liz could tap into the absolute limits of her considerable inner strength to keep pushing through.

And then there was the additional complication of this little thing called COVID. Not resuming her chemo treatments wasn't really an option, even as the entire world shut down. The logistics of getting her in and out of her infusions with as little contact as possible were quite the orchestrated production. She rode the elevator alone, as I was no longer permitted to escort her inside the building, much less keep her company during her treatments. So now, on top of everything else, her long days of treatment were compounded by isolation.

By mid-Spring, though, Liz had made it through. The yearlong cancer treatment treadmill that had us racing from one appointment or consultation to the next finally slowed down. We had to come back to Emory every three months for blood work and scans, but that last chemo treatment was a major milestone in our journey.

That moment came with some raw emotions. Relief, of course. Joy—although because of COVID, we couldn't gather with our friends and family to celebrate. But they once again rallied around us with waves of gifts and heartfelt social media shout-outs. Several friends even put together a mini—parade on our street, driving by to mark the occasion with waves and enthusiastic horn blasts. We sat on the front porch for several hours to soak everything in. It was the most festive day we had enjoyed since all the craziness began the prior summer.

And yet, a new fear emerged from the shadows. Although we were more than ready to turn the page, there had been security in knowing that Liz's every movement was being so closely scrutinized. Being released so suddenly from such a meticulously crafted treatment program, with all of its instructions and boundaries, was oddly stressful. I know that Stockholm syndrome is not the right analogy here, but it's not totally wrong either. As horrible as the past year had been, we had adapted and grown accustomed to our awful reality, and even began to feel, dare I say, comfortable. Now, all of that was being upended.

There's just something about living under someone else's care, where you cede so much control and abdicate so much responsibility for your well-being. Even though it's a bit like being held in captivity, it can also be liberating in a weird way, too. Being released from that captivity left us to fend for ourselves again.

We were headed into the Great Unknown.

After watching all the celebratory videos on Facebook and opening all the gifts, after the last of the cars with the blasting horns had driven off, we sat together on the rug in our living room. We clutched each other, and all the feelings from the past many months burst to the surface. The grief and the triumph. The disbelief and the determination. The fear and the unyielding faith. The gratitude. The boundless love.

We shared heavy tears, both of sadness and joy, overcome by the unbelievably tangled weight of it all.

I re-live this moment often, the two of us locked in an embrace on our living room floor, when the cage doors flew open and we were released back into the wild.

***

Liz and I are eternally grateful to Emory. They saved her life, absolutely, no two ways about it. As a result, we've spent a great amount of time and effort to pay it forward, through fundraising and volunteering and all kinds of other things. We'll be enthusiastic and active Emory supporters forever.

But the one complaint we have now, with the benefit of hindsight, is that we were completely unprepared for the long term emotional trauma. Despite all the warnings about the physical symptoms that would result from Liz's surgery and treatment, there was little to no warning about the mental fall-out. I suspect this is true for many other families who have gone through cancer or other similar health journeys.

On the one hand, I get it. Because we were in a life-or-death crisis, Emory's number one focus was formulating the right treatment and getting her through the surgery. Their mission was to send her home alive. And thank God they aced this part of the test.

But I believe the mental and emotional areas are where the medical profession can do better. I am referring to the entire profession now because I doubt Emory is alone in the way they go about this. Yes, the first priority is to bring the patient home. But focusing on this to the exclusion of everything else is, I would humbly submit, a shortsighted perspective. Because if you believe your patient's mental and emotional states ultimately impact the long-term health prognosis—and there is actual science and data out there to support this idea—then the best treatment plan is one that accounts for the patient's mental health post-surgery. In our case, that starts with giving the patient real information and actionable advice about post-traumatic stress.

To be fair, shortly after we arrived at Emory and confirmed that Liz had the high-grade, we were referred to someone for joint counseling. But those sessions seemed geared toward getting us ready for the surgery and our mounting anxiety as that date approached. Post-surgery, I don't recall a single visit by a psychiatrist or therapist or even being told that we should see one.

That's a problem. There were scores of doctors and specialists in and out of our hospital room before we were discharged. If it was important enough to send in a specialist to discuss caring for the physical scars on Elizabeth's abdomen once they removed her staples (short take: very carefully), then sending in someone to discuss caring for the emotional scars ought to have been a priority, too.

I can't emphasize this last part enough. More attention needs to be given to the mental well-being of cancer patients, and to any patients undergoing high-risk procedures for high-risk diseases. Because while the scars on Liz's abdomen have indeed faded over time, the emotional scarring has been a much trickier proposition.

And corollary to this: the caregivers of these patients need much more mental and emotional support as well.

The trauma of our experience is now a central element of our everyday lives. The shock still sometimes consumes us. We've likened the sensation to standing alongside the road moments after being in a horrendously violent wreck involving scores of piled-up cars, with twisted metal and sirens and plumes of black smoke all around, but there you are... somehow just standing there, intact and alive, wondering *what in the world just happened? And how in the world are we even still here?*

There's just so much to process. It overwhelms you. Your body overdoses on adrenaline and other fight-or-flight chemicals in the moment of that violent collision, and for some—and most certainly for us—the sensation never completely subsides. It may weaken or morph into other things, but the extra adrenaline is always there. Our internal settings are forever changed.

Please don't get me wrong here. I'm not saying we now live somber, joyless lives or that we are mired in a state of stress-induced paralysis. Far from it. The biggest thing we feel nowadays is gratitude, even through the residual emotional strain. There is, in fact, a certain beauty to our new reality, fragmented and fragile as it often seems.

All I'm trying to say is that being told more directly on the front end how profoundly different life would be on the back end could have spared us stress and heartache as we transitioned from survival mode into "now what?" mode. Because confronting the "now what?" has been big and scary and messy. Lots of tough questions. Very few answers.

How can we just snap back into our old lives after everything we've just been through? What is "normal"?

Given everything we know about the risks and tendencies of Liz's disease, how can we be sure this is really over for good? When will the other shoe drop?

And if we do have to go through it all again, will we be as fortunate next time? How did we even make it through the last time?

How much time do we have left together? And how do we prioritize the best use of that time?

We constantly wrestle with these questions, and we come at them from every angle: the practical, the philosophical, and the spiritual.

The first big question above—wondering how we were supposed to just somehow snap back into our old lives—was the easiest to answer. We knew early on we couldn't. That lovely, normal, pre-cancer life of ours is gone forever.

The remaining questions refuse to tap out. Liz's cancer is an aggressive and unpredictable beast, so there really are no definitive answers. We've succumbed to the practical reality of our situation and settled into "we don't know." Immediately followed by "and we probably won't ever know."

Accepting these unknowns is much easier intellectually than it is emotionally or spiritually. But coming to peace with this—admittedly, an ongoing process for us—has led to amazing realizations. There is no other place we would rather be than right here, in this moment. Our life may be scary, yes, and uncertain, too, but we sure are blessed to be sharing it together. There is a profound beauty that comes from viewing your life and time together as the precious commodity that it is.

So. Here we are on the threshold of the wild unknown. Walk with me.

Part Two

WHAT I'VE LEARNED

There've been times in my life

I've been wonderin' why

Still, somehow I believed we'd always survive

"This is It" by Kenny Loggins

Chapter 12
An Update and a Disclaimer

AN IMPORTANT UPDATE ON Liz's health before I pivot to other topics. As of this writing, we are just shy of four years from Liz's initial diagnosis, and a little over three years removed from her surgery and return home from the hospital.

It stirs up an awful lot in both of us to reflect on these milestones. On the one hand, we are profoundly thankful. We've gotten to enjoy three more years together, watching our boys grow and creating memories. We were assured none of those moments. So we seldom miss an opportunity to say thanks for the blessing of additional time.

On the other hand, there is a lingering trauma that is a part of our everyday life. It's tough to make peace with the aggressive and unpredictable nature of Liz's disease. No matter how healthy Liz looks and feels, we know our situation is fragile. And even if we could forget that fact, the stark reminders come every few months: more bloodwork, scans, and follow-up appointments with her oncologist. No matter how joyous the moment we're in, it always seems like we're one bad phone call away.

We ache to move on while knowing there's probably no such thing. Not for us. The dye feels permanently cast.

So at some point, you just have to decide what you're going to choose to make of it all. Because make no mistake: it *is* a choice. And for me, the choice was easy. I decided early on after Liz's diagnosis to accept this was the life Liz and I had been given, to focus as much as I could on the silver linings, and to do the best I could to make something beautiful out of our circumstances.

The trick, of course, is that the *choosing* is easy, but the *doing* is hard. Feelings are complicated things. Sadness and anxiety are powerful forces. You can't will them away, and you can't ignore them either, because they will eventually overrun you in destructive ways. It's big, heavy stuff. And it has to be dealt with.

Coming to this way of thinking was a good news/bad news proposition for me as a caregiver. The good news was that I was (and remain) highly motivated to channel all of this energy and all of these feelings in the best possible way. This mindset was vital, because sometimes, during the dark moments, the only thing you can cling to is your resolve—*no matter what, things are gonna be ok.*

The bad news? I was entirely unprepared to become a caregiver. I don't say this in a self-criticizing way; I don't think anyone could have reasonably anticipated the phone call I received on July 2, 2019. And it's not like there's a manual, either. All I knew was our life had taken a hard left turn, I had been thrust into a new role, and I was going to need to make some drastic adjustments if we were going to make the most of our time.

Because I didn't have many tools at my disposal—not initially, anyway—much of my journey revolved around what I would call deliberative trial and error. Meaning some things I tried early on worked and some didn't, but I was hyper-focused on taking mental notes and giving my various attempts honest appraisals. Basically taking stock of my choices.

The honest self-reflection bit is key, because sometimes the things that work feel out of character for you, and sometimes you have to make tough, uncomfortable choices that differ greatly from those you would have made in your pre-caregiver life. So you have to be unflinchingly honest with yourself. Otherwise, the personal growth part can be elusive or even pass you by altogether.

At some point during my journey, it occurred to me that some of the lessons I was learning were shaping up as a blueprint for more than just coping with the exigencies of the moment. I was transitioning from acting purely on survival instincts to taking a more deliberate look at the bigger picture. Attacking my day and making choices proactively, instead of just reacting to a series of crises.

This shifting of thought was not an overnight thing. But my deliberative trial and error coping process was bringing clarity to my life—and not just through the narrow lens of caregiver. These were life lessons pointing the way to more depth and meaning. And as these little lessons and ideas coalesced in my mind, the origins of this book emerged.

The process of organizing these thoughts on paper has been a therapeutic one. I have re-lived some tough moments, absolutely. But I have also taken comfort in the lessons learned, found beauty in the silver linings, and reaffirmed my commitment to faith.

So if any part of this book can make a difference to someone else—whether caregiver or someone in any moment of struggle—then all the better. Because I've benefitted so greatly from leaning on my support network over these past few years, the idea of paying any small bit of it forward is a humbling one. Perhaps some of this will speak to you.

Before jumping in to all of this, though, the lawyer in me must offer a few disclaimers. I'm going to touch on some wide-ranging topics over these next few chapters—from physical fitness, to spirituality, to therapy and self-care. I'm going to offer commentary and advice on these topics, and I've got some deeply ingrained opinions about how these concepts have served me through my journey, and how some of what I have learned might help other people, too.

But make no mistake here: I am not an expert on these topics. Nor do I profess to be. I am not a theologian, physical therapist, psychotherapist, or grief counselor. Sure, I've now done a fair amount of reading, and I've absorbed some basic knowledge while seeking help from the real experts in these fields. But that does not make me the expert—and I don't want anyone reading this to construe my advice as such. I'm just a guy who found himself thrust into a challenging set of circumstances and set out to find his way through it.

This leads to a related disclaimer. The anecdotes and observations below reflect what has worked for *me*. Settling into the role of a caregiver is not a "one size fits all" proposition, and some of what I cover (and I'm thinking primarily about spirituality here) may be deeply polarizing. I get that. So I am not presuming to have all the answers here.

That said, I strongly feel that some of this is universal. For example, the next chapter: "Taking Care of Yourself." While I don't typically trade in absolutes, *taking care of yourself* is unquestionably necessary. Whatever your idea of self-care—video games, playing clarinet, soaking in ice-baths—if you don't take care of yourself, you will fail not only yourself but also those around you who need your help. While the type of self-care may vary (and while the examples below are particular to me), the underlying message applies.

And so, my twelve hundred word wind-up complete, I offer you the ideas that have sustained me and the lessons I have learned.

Chapter 13
Taking Care of Yourself

You Both Carry the Weight

BEING A CAREGIVER COMES with great pressures and demands, but it is not without its rewards. Although there are many raw moments of wishing things had played out differently, those feelings do not prevent me from being grateful for the many little blessings we have found along the way. In fact, the ability to appreciate the silver linings buried within the thunderclouds has been one of the most important factors to maintaining our happiness and sanity.

One unanticipated silver lining? Making new friends. Travelling this path has opened doors to new communities we would not have otherwise found—patients, caregivers, and others impacted by cancer or other profound health challenges. Since July 2, 2019, Liz and I have made a whole new network of friends to learn from. And lean on.

One such friend is a guy we met as Liz was winding down her chemotherapy treatments in 2020. He was a member of our synagogue and a Rabbi at our Temple introduced us to him (over Zoom, because this was during the early days of the pandemic) as part of an informal study group. We also shared a few mutual friends with the guy, so there was comfort and familiarity from the get-go.

But we had much more in common than just mutual friends. Our new friend also had a firsthand encounter with cancer. Midway through our first Zoom visit, as we were still getting to know each other and getting our bearings with the study materials, we learned that years ago he too had served as a caregiver for a wife with cancer. We also learned his story ended tragically. His wife was no longer with him. They had a small child together who lost his mother.

I'm not going to lie to you—trying to take in this information from our new friend as he was sharing it in real time over Zoom was a take-your-breath-away moment. And for a split second, I almost clicked the "leave meeting" button on our iPad. This was an awful lot of unexpected information. Maybe a little too close to home and too painful to engage.

On top of that, I had a weird, irrational survivor's guilt wash over me in that moment. Even though the scars from Liz's surgery were still raw and her health was still fragile, and even though we were both still terribly frightened... I felt guilty. Sharing my honest feelings of grief and fear and sadness with our new friend—after all that he had been through—somehow seemed ungrateful and obtuse. Liz and I made quick eye contact, and I am certain she was thinking the same thing.

But the moment of panic passed, and Liz and I found ourselves sharing with our brand new friend intimate details of the past year—of Liz's diagnosis, the brutality of her surgery, and our subsequent struggles to return to normalcy. We put it all out there. While her surgery may have been a medical success, the lingering effects of her cancer were everywhere. Learning how to live with the aftermath of her cancer was the overriding challenge consuming us. We had just met this guy fifteen minutes ago, and we were choking through every tough emotion.

And then he responded. It was one of those "etched in your brain forever" moments. After listening intently for several minutes about things that must have stirred up all kinds of painful feelings for him, our new friend responded with this: "Guys. Don't just call this 'Liz's cancer.' Because that's not what it is. Coming from someone who has been there... cancer is something that both of you carry. You *both* are living with cancer."

He looked utterly serious. "*Both*."

I replay that exchange often in my mind. It's one of the many little insights I've spent hours pondering, and that ultimately led me to write this book. Because *both of you are living with cancer* is so much more than a semantic point. Of course, cancer originated in Liz's body, but its impact extends well beyond her own physical domain and now touches on just about every detail of our lives. It goes from the mundane (what kinds of condiments we buy or sunscreens we use) to how we pray (rigorously and often). The impact is ever-present, and as much as you want it not to define your lives, the imprint is permanent. Even though we go to great lengths to protect our everyday joy, cancer has reset the reality of our lives.

But allowing myself to accept this idea of "our" cancer has been a liberating paradigm shift. After all, Liz and I are in this together and I am sometimes sad and frightened, too.

I'm sure there's an outdated school of thought which maintains that the caregiver must maintain an even-keeled approach at all times and at all costs. The old *she needs you to stay strong!* mindset. And sure, there were moments when the job called for that—when things were so frightening and unsteady that I needed to be the voice of calm and the shoulder for Liz to cry on.

But it's not realistic to expect that of myself at all times, in total disregard of everything inside me that makes me a sentient human being. Because there have been many moments during this journey—too many, candidly—when I have tried to suppress my anxiety. Or, if I'm really being honest, suppress my anger at how this could have happened.

But I've learned that refusing to acknowledge those feelings does nothing but create internal turmoil and panic. Giving myself license to "feel the feels" (as Liz puts it) has allowed me to grow in a healthier, more clear-headed way. Much more on this in a bit.

Taking Care of Your Body

The first few weeks after Liz's diagnosis, we kept it pretty quiet. We weren't sure what we were facing and the thought of telling others about it was too difficult for us emotionally. So, except for family and a few close friends, we kept our painful secret to ourselves.

But once we were ready and started to share, word traveled fast—because Liz has a huge family and we both have decent-sized personal and professional networks from living in the same community for so long. Once we told a few folks, it wasn't long before all kinds of gifts and notes and other thoughtful gestures came pouring in.

Some were pragmatic (comfy socks, sweatshirts, and blankets for the many hours Liz would spend in chemotherapy sessions), while others were more spirits-lifting (books and cards and such). They ran the gamut. The daughter of one of Liz's overseas coworkers—a talented, thoughtful teen whom Liz had never met or even heard of—painted Liz a watercolor portrait featuring a woman, dressed in white, standing in a field of wildflowers with the sun shining optimistically above.

And, of course, food. Enormous amounts. There was a "food train" of meals arriving daily—a concept that, I'll confess, I had never heard of before Liz's diagnosis. We could barely keep up with it. But thank goodness for this edible Amtrak service, because with all the appointments and procedures and tests we had going on, it was an incredible lifeline to not have to devote time or headspace to planning dinner for the family.

The meals and gifts kept rolling in. Every day, there was a pile of boxes and dishes and envelopes waiting for us when we got home. Our daily delivery of support and thoughtfulness and hope. It was both humbling and a little overwhelming.

Then, something a little different. One day, a package arrived addressed not to Liz or even the both of us, but just to me. Inside was a small box. And inside that box was a canister of multi-vitamins and a note from one of Liz's oldest and dearest college friends. The message: *I love you guys. I'm thinking of you. But you're in for a long ride, so please take care of yourself, too.*

While much of the first several weeks after Liz's diagnosis remains a clouded blur, that small box stands out. I'm beyond thankful for it. Because when your adrenaline revs up and your world spirals, it can be pretty easy to lose sight of the importance of this advice. *Take care of yourself.*

It may seem counterintuitive to put any focus on me, considering everything Liz was going through. But when you stop and think about it, it makes all the sense in the world. So much weight was being hoisted on my shoulders—both emotionally and practically speaking—that I needed to be at my absolute strongest to withstand the pressure. My self-care wasn't just important for my own health. The bigger takeaway is that everyone needed me to invest in my well-being.

There are many layers to this concept of self-care, but the easiest place to start is with physical health. For the caregiver, it has to be a priority both for its own sake—long periods of stress inevitably take a physical toll—but also as a necessary pathway for emotional health.

You don't need to be a licensed psychotherapist to recognize the benefits of exercise to address stress and restlessness. In fact, you'd probably be hard-pressed to find a credible health care professional who would try to argue otherwise. So this bit of advice is pretty much a given for anyone, and doubly so if you're hardwired like I am. Physical activity has been a huge part of my life since the day I started walking, and it has served as a reliable stress management outlet for me during every stage of my life. So no hard sell here. Once I was jolted into consciousness by the "take care of yourself" gesture, it did not require a huge internal leap for me to buy-in. It was exactly the prodding I needed.

But when would I find the time? And where? And how? Saying "take care of yourself" sounds great in theory, but the practical constraints we were facing as a family were pretty imposing. Obviously, there was the foremost concern of caring for Liz, which was a huge allotment of time both before her surgery (with the endless cycle of medical appointments) and afterwards (when she needed significant hands-on care).

And then, of course, there were my kids and my deeply rooted need to serve not just as a chaperone or taskmaster but, even more importantly, as a steady emotional presence. To pull that off, you have to physically be there. There are no shortcuts to assuring your kids you are still there, mentally present, and dialed-in to their needs. Especially when they were at such a young age and no doubt confused by everything going on.

On top of all that, there was the not-insignificant matter of trying to keep up with a busy law practice. Being pulled in all these different directions meant finding time to exercise or engage in other forms of self-care was going to be a difficult task, indeed. It's exhausting just thinking about it, even in hindsight.

But the good news is, it's not impossible. There wasn't really a magic formula for making it happen, but for me it boiled down to two things. One: I was going to make this a priority no matter what. Two: I would be really, really creative and flexible to make it happen. Part of this "being creative" involved holistic time management hacks, which I'll detail in later chapters. As for the time itself, there were a few guiding principles I put to work and still carry with me today.

First, I decided that whenever free time presented itself, I would always be prepared. Key to this approach was expunging from my mind the notion that I could ever fit in "traditional" workouts in any kind of predictable, consistent fashion. Sure, there were days when I had a block of an hour or two to make something like taking a class or lifting weights at the Y happen, but those opportunities were rare. So rather than allowing my mess of a schedule to prevent me from working out altogether—a trap that not just caregivers but also countless busy professionals can probably relate to—I promised myself that even if it was only for 15 minutes, I was going to make myself do something active every day.

Rather than falling into the trap of thinking I couldn't afford the time to exercise, I turned the concept inside out. I told myself I couldn't afford *not* to find the time to exercise.

During the first year after Liz's diagnosis, my workout regimen didn't resemble anything a personal trainer or fitness professional would come up with. But it ably served the purpose of keeping my body moving and my headspace as clear as it could be under the circumstances. I woke up every morning and told myself no matter what the day had in store, I was going to carve out a little time—even if only a few minutes—just for myself. And that I would get my sweat and blood flowing as much as possible within the constraints of the day.

Although I am not a regimented person by nature when it comes to mapping out my workouts, I recognized the situation was calling for me to engage in a little more day-to-day preparation. So I was always ready if the opportunity for a quick workout presented itself. I kept a gym bag in my car at all times, which contained workout clothes, swim goggles, a water bottle, and a towel. Unless I absolutely couldn't for some reason (a client meeting, for example), I always wore running shoes or at least shoes I could work out in (my trusted Vans). I was, in a word, ready.

And I tell you what, when those opportunities presented themselves—no matter how tight the window—I went for it. The out of office meeting I expected to be two hours but lasted only an hour? Straight to the gym. Or the pool. Or just straight outside wherever I was for a quick run/walk and light cardio session. Suddenly, I was "that guy" who just dropped and banged out pushups in random places—park, hospital, indoors, outdoors. Sure, there were moments when I felt all kinds of self-conscious about it, but if you start from the mindset of "I-am-making-this-happen-no-matter-what" and work backward from there, you will come up with all kinds of inventive ways to get there.

For example, scheduling calls. If a call didn't require me to present or take notes—administrative work meetings, seminars, or personal stuff—I would dial in from an exercise bike, hit mute, and log some miles. If I was out for a run or on the stationary bike and an unexpected call came in from a client or another lawyer who wanted to talk work, I would answer but right away explain what I was doing and ask if they were cool with my multitasking. Sometimes I got a "let's connect later" kind of response, but surprisingly there were many more times when whoever was calling gladly obliged, and I would dial it back just enough to think and speak clearly without having to shut it down altogether.

Besides making the time for exercise, I also prioritized sleep when I was able. It wasn't always easy, of course, especially in the first year after Liz's diagnosis. But I structured a good many of my daily habits to keep sleep top of mind. I turned in pretty early most nights—usually shortly after we put the boys down—unless Liz wanted to stay up and talk.

I'd also grab quick naps wherever and whenever I could. Because my nighttime sleep was so erratic during that first year, if I found myself drifting off during the day, I'd just roll with it instead of trying to fight it. Sometimes I would close my door at work, prop my feet up on my desk, and set an alarm on my phone for ten or fifteen minutes. Other times, especially when I was out of the office anyway and didn't have a work call or whatever to address, I'd run home for a quick nap before heading back into the office. I accepted the fact that trying to be "productive" (at least in today's sense of the term, anyway) for every minute of every day was pointless and I would cause myself (and, by extension, my family) more problems if I was exhausted and burned out.

***

Before pivoting to the next topic—taking care of your emotional well being—there is one other aspect of this exercise piece that I have to hit. And it is one that translates into a broader life lesson, caregiver or not. Exercise symbolizes something important. No matter where you are in your life and no matter what outside forces may be impacting your time and attention, you've got to save a bit of yourself for you.

So much of being a caregiver is about re-framing your focus and life priorities. Obviously, everything changed for us on July 2, 2019. How we view things. Work/life balance. Retirement. The timeline for checking things off our bucket list. Directly or indirectly, Liz's health weighs on every big decision we make. And many of the smaller ones, too.

I want to be really clear that I'm not complaining. I often say that being a caregiver to Liz is the greatest job in the world, because it means I get to be the one by her side. I mean it. I wouldn't trade places with anyone. But, in the spirit of being totally transparent, the caregiver role comes with some other things, too. Including having to re-think all of your previous priorities and life plans to make space for all the unexpected changes.

Again, not a complaint, but neither is it insignificant to let go of your old self. It's one of the most difficult parts of the caregiver gig.

So this is where the exercise time comes in for me and why it holds so much power. Above and beyond the physical health benefits and stress relief, it is about creating a tiny space in my life that I still can claim as my own.

My exercise time is one of the few times during my day where I can be totally selfish and guilt-free about it. I get to make it just about me. No matter how quick or how long the workout cycle is on whatever day, it is *my* time. Not time to focus on Liz, or my boys, or the responsibilities of my job, or anything else. Just me. Feeling the sensation of my body moving, the sound of my heartbeat, and however much sweat I can muster in the time I have cleared out. Me time.

Even if only a few minutes, it's precious.

A cool little story to close this point out. For the few years leading up to the summer of 2019, I got into short-distance triathlons. I had always been a runner, and by late 2015 I started getting into biking and swimming, too. So I started competing in these short-distance races (known as sprint triathlons) and I *loved* them. The adrenaline rush. The sense of accomplishment. And the sprint distance was perfect. I had to train some, sure, but I could still balance the training regimen with the time constraints of raising two very young boys and practicing law. For a few years there, working toward my next race became a big weekend focus.

By early 2019, I decided I was ready for the next challenge: a longer race known as the Olympic distance triathlon. These typically consist of a one mile swim, a 20-ish mile bike ride, and a 6 mile run. Basically, twice the distance of the sprint races. It was a stretch goal for sure, but the boys were getting old enough where I felt like I could pull it off without putting too much of an unfair burden on Liz while training.

By Spring 2019, I was eyeing races in the late August/early September timeframe and increasing my training and mileage while I looked for a race that would fit our schedule. Liz was 100% behind the idea and it was an exciting goal to think about and plan for.

But then my office phone rang on July 2, 2019, and those plans evaporated. This was something that would never happen, or at least not anytime soon, anyway. Not that it even mattered. Because once I got that call, training for an Olympic distance triathlon was a silly luxury I had zero time to worry about.

But life dreams can be a stubborn thing to let go of, and as Liz regained her strength and stamina post-surgery, the thoughts of an Olympic triathlon crept back into my mind. 2020 was out of the question for a host of reasons (including COVID, of course), but by late Spring 2021, things were shifting for us. I'm not saying we were "out of the woods," because from a cancer perspective, that's a complicated conversation. But in terms of Liz's recovery, we had definitely turned a corner. The days of frailty and near-constant exhaustion were well behind us, and with each passing day, she looked and seemed more and more like the healthy and energetic Liz of old.

So when I casually mentioned one day that I was thinking about giving the Olympic tri another shot, Liz was once again totally behind in. No surprise there. In fact, she started actively pushing me to do it.

So I had a buddy help me map out a training program and started putting in the work. Six days a week of tough programming. Sixty minute bike rides on a stationary trainer followed by long runs through the neighborhood in the dark. Tough, monotonous laps in the pool. My home and work demands still came first, of course, but whatever I had left, I poured into my training regimen.

Even though it was a lot, I kept going. On top of the physical toll, this was tough administratively. There were bi-weekly 4AM wake-up alarms so I could train early enough to manage the morning breakfast and school drop-off routine with our boys. And because I hadn't been training consistently for the year-plus prior, I was constantly sore. But I got the running and biking miles in, along with the seemingly endless laps in the pool, and by the end of the summer I was ready.

And I did it! In September 2021, after all those hard months of training, I crossed the finish line for my very first Olympic triathlon. I certainly didn't set any course records, but I plodded through and managed a respectable time for my age group. It was exhilarating. The triumph of accomplishing something I had been wanting to try for years.

To the point of this chapter... it also was something *just for me.*

Although I should also add that Liz and the boys were cheering at the finish line to celebrate with me. Just because the accomplishment was something I wanted for myself does not mean I didn't want to share the joy with them afterwards. I'm going to take care of myself, yes, but we're all in this together. I couldn't imagine it any other way.

Taking Care of Your Emotional Well-Being

The other part of the self-care regimen is to prioritize your emotional well-being.

There is a lot that could be said here. So much so that it is difficult to know where to begin. Also, because I lack any kind of mental health credentials, I am a leery of exploring this subject too deeply for fear of giving unqualified advice. Besides, I'm guessing there are a great many books out there offering sage advice on this topic.

And yet, this is far too important a topic to skip past altogether. Because there is no untangling the role of caregiver from the mental and emotional strain the role entails. If you neglect your mental well-being, you'll ultimately fail not just yourself but also the ones you're supposed to be caring for. That's certainly how I saw it once I realized it was time for me to seek professional help.

Perhaps that's the best place to start: recognizing that your own mental health needs to be a priority. Yeah, recognition being the initial step is kind of obvious. But it's necessary. Simply admitting: *I need help.*

For me, that moment of clarity came when we were still trying to understand the origins of Liz's cancer and told that genetic testing was in order. Instantly, the reach of my worry expanded not just to Liz but also to our boys. That moment was monumental, and proved too big for me. While I had managed until that point to keep my wits about me and my stress and trauma more or less compartmentalized, I knew I needed professional help to keep the stress and fear and sadness from overrunning me.

In hindsight, I probably should have come to this realization sooner than I did. I'm not saying this with regret or to second guess my every move during those first several weeks—Lord knows, I was doing the best I could—but as a lead-in to the next point here. If you are wondering whether you might benefit from talking to a professional, you probably should. This is true both for caregiving specifically and for life challenges generally. I recognize seeking this kind of help can impose costs, both in terms of money and time. I don't wish to minimize that at all. But left unattended, the cost of emotional distress will be far greater.

The good news is we are now living in a time when being open about the need for tending to our mental health no longer comes with the same stigma it once did. There are several examples of high-profile individuals—professional athletes, entertainers, and even politicians—who have shared deeply personal accounts about their mental struggles and the importance of seeking help. While admitting to the need for help was once unfairly viewed as a sign of weakness or failure, the script seems to be flipping to where it is now applauded as an act of emotional maturity and courage. This is a *great* thing. So don't be afraid to go there.

One other thing about seeking professional help. This may seem like another obvious bit of advice, but be sure to shop around. I spoke to a couple of people before eventually landing with the person I currently work with. There wasn't anything "wrong" about any of the first couple of counselors I spoke to; quite the contrary, I'll always be thankful for the time I spent with them. But talking to a professional is a deeply personal thing, so if it feels anything less than exactly right for you in that setting, it may be worth visiting with another person to see if the energy feels a more comfortable to you.

***

So that's the first piece: acknowledging the need for help and then going out and getting it. But that's not all it takes to tend to your emotional well-being. At least not for me. Because while talking to a professional has helped me work through and process much of the stress and anxiety, it is not a magic pill, and it doesn't mean those negative thoughts and feelings vanish altogether. It just gives me better tools for managing the day-to-day ups and downs.

This is important to understand. While therapy can be a useful tool, you can't view it as the only proper time or place to confront your feelings and deal with them. Of course, therapy sessions can be extraordinarily cathartic, but it is a mistake to bottle everything up during the time in between sessions. I say this from experience. I tried it, and it was not an effective way of managing my stress levels or coping with my anxiety and sadness.

Eventually, I decided to give myself permission to be real about how I was feeling about everything we were going through. In other words, embracing the fact that sometimes I was going to be stressed, or saddened, or frightened, and that was an entirely normal and permissible way to feel. No longer would I keep everything locked in an emotional vault until I was in the presence of my therapist

Again, in hindsight, this sounds like such an obvious bit of wisdom, but if you're a dude my age, there's a lot of societal-driven programming that you have to override to give yourself that permission. Doubly so if you are a lawyer-litigator, where any sign of these feelings is usually taken as a sign of weakness.

But I'm well past that now. I've given myself permission, in today's parlance, to "feel the feels" and just be OK with it.

Let's unpack that.

Being Real About the Feels

Because I have never attempted to write a book before, I can't say I know much about the "traditional" or "best" way to approach such endeavors. Nor did I attempt to learn much about it before jumping in, other than to ask a few other writers I know how they enjoyed the experience and whether they had any bits of wisdom to impart. If there are rules of thumb or best practices for the book-writing process, even after completing this book you are now holding, I remain in the dark as to those insights.

So, with this "blank slate" approach of mine in mind, let me provide a little insight into how I went about writing this book. (I promise there will eventually be a point to all of this.)

The one word description would be "haphazardly." As in, there was not a lot of well-designed structure or process when I decided to start writing. I just sort of went for it, hoping ideas would coalesce into a structure.

The slightly longer version would be: "I started this book with an outline and broad concepts in mind, but then jumped around backward and forward filling in the details."

And the still more detailed description would be: "As I was writing, I jumped around from chapter to chapter and idea to idea as time and my mood warranted." Some ideas and chapters formed quickly (the opening chapter, for example, and the section on taking care of your physical health), while other chapters were much harder to write (like the chapters about Liz's surgery or the upcoming chapter on faith and spirituality).

I never attempted to approach this all in the order it now appears. Instead, on any given day, I wrote what I felt, trusting I would eventually get to everything and then tie it all neatly together. Because I was committed to doing this by feel. The one promise I made to myself was to go all in. This had to be in my honest voice, without filter or posture or pretense. Otherwise, it wouldn't be worth the effort.

But real talk: this commitment to go all-in—this level of soul-baring—is terrifying. Frequently while I was writing—indeed, right now as I write these very words—I had a creeping worry about how exposing this all is. And an insecurity about being judged.

So this commitment to authenticity is why I wrote this book haphazardly and out of sequence. Because while I can write with relative ease about workouts or otherwise recite certain basic background facts about our journey, it is not nearly as easy to strip off the armor and dig down to the bottom of what it all means. It leaves you vulnerable. To really go there, you have to (a) be in the time and headspace where it feels safe to strip down, and (b) allow yourself the time to let the truly deep stuff rise to the surface.

All to say, this section—*Getting Real With the Feels*—is my stripping-of-armor moment. It was the most difficult section in the book to write because it is the most personally revealing, even though that revelation is one of the primary drivers for writing this thing in the first place.

I've already covered much of the emotional strain that comes with being a caregiver—the fear, the stress, the grief. Anyone who thinks about it probably assumes these feelings are simply part of the deal. But a big part of what I have learned—and what can sometimes be hard to come to terms with—is how much deeper it goes than mere feelings. It goes all the way down. To the bottom. To your core identity.

I alluded to this when describing the symbolic importance of training for the Olympic triathlon. For me, the most profound thing about being a caregiver is letting go of my old self and becoming something—someone?—different. The moment I picked up the phone in my office on July 2, 2019, my purpose and focus in life irrevocably altered. And no matter how far we eventually distance ourselves from that shattering moment, there is no going back to my old life. My previous identity has been permanently replaced by a new one.

It's a profound thing to say goodbye to your old self. To genuinely let go of who you thought you were. To re-prioritize everything else happening in your world. Just because I wouldn't choose to trade places with anyone else in the world (because really, I wouldn't) doesn't mean there aren't sacrifices associated with being a caregiver. Because absolutely there are. And there is a bumpy, painful process involved in coming to peace with that. A process defined by dark thoughts and darker impulses:

Why us?

Why me?

How can this all be so unfair?

Why can't I have my old life back?

Sometimes you feel horribly selfish and ungrateful asking yourself these kinds of questions, but any caregiver who claims they've never wrestled with these thoughts is probably not being emotionally honest. At some point, no matter how faith-oriented or otherwise grateful you are, human nature kicks in and these moments of anguished handwringing become unavoidable.

Heading down that path in your mind can lead to anger, which I don't like owning up to. It's quite the unflattering look. But the combination of "*why us*" or "*why me*" thinking, when mixed in with other stressors in your life, can lead to things boiling over in drastic ways.

There was a particularly charged work-related incident for me in the Summer of 2020, right as Liz was getting off chemo and still struggling on many fronts. I was trying to settle a case for a client, but we were bumping up against a fast approaching deadline. It was late in the afternoon and we needed resolution by close of business that day. The stakes were high, and I was bouncing from one call to the next, trying to nail down all the final details.

I was working from home on this particular day, and while these work calls were happening Eli and Isaac were in the living room having a spirited battle with their Legoland Styrofoam swords. The noise and commotion was a problem, because Liz was in our guest bedroom upstairs and I was trying to get her some rest. Not easy with the boys stampeding around. It was also annoying and distracting, as you can imagine, with them carrying on as I was trying to work the phones and figure my way out of the legal maze. My kids are legitimately adorable, but sometimes they are wild animals.

To escape all the commotion just for a second, I took a call in my bedroom closet and prayed that the boys would heed my admonition to keep the noise to a dull roar and stay downstairs long enough for me to wrap things up. The call was tense from the jump. Right away, one of the lawyers representing the other side reminded me of the time-sensitivity of the situation: "Your client is out of time." He was polite and professional, but firm and, honestly, one hundred percent correct about all of it.

That's when the pressure finally got to me. I lost it. Flipped my lid. Erupted. And I let everyone on that call know—and there were quite a few of us, calling in from three different cities—that they needed to BACK OFF because I was simultaneously trying to care for my ailing wife with my two kids screaming at each other in the background AND I WAS DOING THE BEST I COULD, DAMNIT! Suddenly, I was louder than anything my boys were doing in the living room. I could feel my heart throbbing in my temples as I shouted.

This moment was a low point for me professionally.

Of course, law can be a stressful gig and there are sometimes going to be high-pressure situations you just have to work your way through. I've been in the courtroom enough over the past two decades to become comfortable with that part of the job description. And no matter how tense the moment, I've never been much of a yeller—whether in a professional setting or otherwise—and I often think less of those who practice that way. Win or lose, you're supposed to represent the profession in a dignified way. I'm big on that.

Yet, there I was, standing in my bedroom closet, shouting at a whole crowd of lawyers and dragging in all kinds of impertinent emotional baggage. In that raw moment, I lashed out like a frightened, petulant child. Which, as I reflect on it, I kind of was. There was a confluence of too much pressure from too many directions bearing down on me all at once. The prediction I had served up in my lawyer-in-distress email one year earlier had finally come true: I totally lost my shit.

The Type A Litigator in me feels compelled to report that I eventually regained my wits, and the moment passed. We salvaged the deal and the client was happy. Later, I called the other lawyers to apologize, and they were all really gracious about it. But, happy ending notwithstanding, I am still embarrassed when I think back on this incident.

And I wish I could say this was the only occasion of its kind, but it wasn't. It wasn't an everyday thing or even a frequent thing, but there was a real out-of-character hot streak during this stage of our journey that occasionally got the best of me. Moments where I lost my patience and snapped at the boys just for being noisy, active children. Political discussions that started out politely enough before quickly overheating. Other random, weird moments where, for whatever reason, my typically measured demeanor gave way to quick-flash anger.

Because sometimes I *was* angry. Plain and simple. Not so much at my boys or opposing counsel or whatever else it was that happened to be the final straw in whatever moment I was in, but rather at the direction our life had taken. This was frightening and painful, and it wasn't supposed to happen to us. Not to Liz. Not to the life we had dreamed of together. When everything you hold dear and build your life around feels like it's being taken away from you, you get pissed. At nothing. At everything. At the world.

During the first few years of our journey, I did a fabulous job of keeping it cool and all together... until the moments I didn't.

Those moments are brutal. When your number one job, above all else, is to stay steady and in control and you feel like you've failed? Like you've let down everyone who was counting on you? When that happens—and if you're a caregiver for long enough, it probably will—all you can do is pick yourself back up and try to learn something from it. Then forgive yourself and move on. Because your people still need you.

***

As Liz and I walk further and further down this new path of our life together, the meaning of my caregiver role has shifted. From

July 2019 through the first full year following Liz's surgery, my role as a "caregiver" was what the term most directly connotes: escorts to far too many doctor's appointments, hands-on care, and a significantly increased hands-on role with Eli and Isaac. The role required daily, physical presence.

But, as time passes, the role ends up going well beyond the physical. The shift in my heart and mindset lives on. Although Liz doesn't require hands-on care these days, the older version of me is gone. I am still Liz's caregiver—and always will be—even if now in a much different way than I once was. The reminders are everywhere.

When Liz tosses and turns in bed at night with the worries of the unknown—which she still often does—I am reminded.

When we sit to discuss our future plans, with our altered timelines and work horizons, and when we wrestle with the tough, existential questions of how to best prioritize every precious minute of our time... I am reminded.

While we are awaiting the results of her upcoming round of bloodwork and scans, with our hands clasped tight and holding our collective breath, I am reminded.

When I pray, which is often, it is in a caregiver's voice and spoken from a caregiver's heart. I am still often consumed by thoughts of Liz's health and the fragility of it all.

And there are so many other examples of how my life is impacted by these reminders. When Liz calls me at an unexpected time (for example, if she knows I have something on my calendar at that moment but calls anyway), I'll jump with a surge of adrenaline. Unless I absolutely cannot, I always pick it up. I've excused myself from meetings, depositions, work-outs, and every other situation you can imagine just to hear Liz's voice and her assurance that everything is ok. Definitely a caregiver in those moments, too.

I drop the boys off at school most days. On days when I know Liz is still getting ready at home, I usually swing back by the house after the school drop-off just to see her and squeeze her one more time before I head into the office. And to tell her how much I love her.

I'm driven by the need to make the most of every minute with her, and the most of every minute the four of us have together as a family, making memories.

I mean it when I say being a caregiver is the greatest gig in the world. It truly is. But believing that doesn't make it a stress or worry-free endeavor. I've learned the tough lesson that gratitude and fright can co-exist. It's a lesson you have to learn if you're going to effectively take care of yourself.

More on gratitude later, but we're not done with the hard stuff. Obviously, there is the struggle with existential worry. It was never a major issue for me before, but it is a fact of life now. Just to be clear: I'm not saying I lived a worry-free life before July 2, 2019, because of course I had to manage work-related stress and general life stress just like everyone else.

But prior to July 2, 2019, my baseline skewed on the low-stress side—especially as I aged and benefited from added life experience. Things had been good and steady for me for a lot of years before the lightning bolt struck. We had built a beautiful, love-filled life for ourselves and were enormously thankful for it.

Now, that low-stress baseline has been flipped in the other direction. I say this even with the years of immediate crisis being in the rearview mirror. I don't wish to be melodramatic, but thoughts of Liz's health and all the unknowns weigh down hard on us. It's impossible for it not to considering what we know.

And this stress can have very real physiological manifestations. Sleeplessness and tension headaches were never a thing for me before, but they sure are now. The same with seemingly unprovoked mood swings and hot streaks. My mind and body feel different. They *are* different. These new sensations tell me I'm a different person.

Here's the thing about that. I've come to learn that anxiety is rarely rational, and it does not respect boundaries. Liz's health may often be the root cause of my anxiety, but once my anxiety level gets ramped up, the sensation often extends beyond thoughts about Liz's health. When I'm amped up or on edge, it spills into my feelings about everything else in my life: work, my boys, all of it. You work hard to chase the clouds away.

Fortunately, I have made progress in identifying the triggers, which helps me understand my moods and brace for emotional dips. A big one is the anniversary of Liz's diagnosis. On the one hand, that day is a well-earned milestone of triumph. But on the other, it can also conjure up sad and frightening feelings. I'll sometimes argue with myself about which side of the telescope I should look through: the side that says we have been the beneficiaries of a great miracle for which we should be eternally thankful, or the side that says we have suffered a huge, still-unfolding tragedy and are living on borrowed time. Thankfully, it's the former perspective that prevails 85% of the time, but it would be dishonest to pretend like Liz and I don't stare down from the edge of the abyss from time to time.

Another trigger is hearing about the cancer struggles of others. Certainly, you don't have to be a cancer patient or caregiver to have empathy for that situation. Everyone who hears about something like that gets sad on some level. But hearing those stories from the vantage point of someone already steeped in all the subtexts of that journey—the shock and disorientation, the dread, the emotional and physical exhaustion—those feelings ratchet up tenfold. You literally feel the pain that the other family is going through. And that is, of course, yet another reminder that we are still on our journey, too.

In August 2020, Chadwick Boseman—award-winning actor and star of the Marvel movie *Black Panther*—passed away from colon cancer. It was shocking news, because he had never spoken publicly about his illness and apparently very few people outside of his family knew he was ill. He was a shining light in the film industry and, at 43 years of age, he was suddenly gone. The story dominated the headlines for weeks.

The news gutted me. Obviously, it was tragic in its own right, and I was hardly alone in feeling sad about the loss. Chadwick Boseman was a beloved film icon and trailblazer, because out of the seemingly hundreds of Marvel movies released over the past decade, *Black Panther* was the first to feature an African American lead protagonist. His ascension into that role was a big deal culturally and socially, and his megawatt smile and larger-than-life charisma made him just the right guy for the superhero role and everything the moment signified. This was a huge loss.

For Liz and me, though, Chadwick Boseman's passing also hit uncomfortably close to home. We were barely one year outside of Liz's diagnosis and only a few short months removed from completing her chemotherapy. Basically, we were still very much in the thick of our fight. And here we find this beautiful, talented soul—befitting of the cinematic superhero he played—had just lost that same battle. He was only a few years older than Liz and left a grieving spouse behind. He had a family and an entire unfinished life ahead.

As hard as I tried to remain thankful and faithful and positive in the aftermath of that news, my mind couldn't help but go to the darkest of places… *Cancer spares no one. Not even superheroes.*

I bottomed out. Badly. The fight-or-flight adrenaline rush that I had gotten pretty good at managing came surging back. I was on edge and irascible and it spilled over into work, my interactions with Liz and the boys, and just about everything else happening around me. It felt like a tidal wave had flung me all the way back to the beginning.

I had fallen into dark depths and was struggling to swim back to the surface.

This episode scared me because it was my first major breakdown after Liz completed her chemotherapy. I hadn't expected an aftershock like this, and it lasted for weeks.

But even worse, I felt powerless to slow the downward spiral. In high-stress situations, I'm usually able to talk myself off the ledge just through mental resilience (the old "fake it till you make it" approach). But when that typically reliable tool fails you, it can feel like a free fall. Like drowning. This was a tough lesson I was learning: sometimes all you can do is hold on until the feeling passes.

Over time, aided by therapy and paying heed to the lessons I had learned about self-care, things stabilized. The moment passed, and I began to feel like my old self again. This has been the trend for the past few years. I'll find myself going to a dark place, but then I'll do the work and find a way to get turned back toward the light.

I'm still making my peace with this pattern. I don't like it, but trigger moments are inevitable and, just as with swimming into a real riptide, if you thrash about fighting the current, you may end up exhausting yourself and doing more harm than good. But I've gotten to a place where even if my inner rational voice can't turn the feelings of the moment off, it can contextualize them. Which takes at least some of the angst away and turns the volume down.

"*It's ok, Matt. It's just your adrenaline fueling this. It is a physical response to normal feelings of fear and sadness that flow from a very real trauma. Allow yourself to feel that, but stay positive, too. Trust. Love. You will come out on the other side. Just as you and Liz always do.*"

This inner pep talk, which to this day I still give myself from time to time, is not an immediate cure-all. I don't instantly snap back into a Zen-like tranquility. But it helps keep the feelings contained, and I have found it is far better to allow myself to acknowledge them than to torture myself with guilt or shame over having those moments. Being real about the feels means being kind to yourself and allowing honest space for the harder feelings and moments.

Consider Finding Yourself a Caregiver or Other Form of Support

In the Fall of 2021, about one year after Chadwick Boseman's passing, I had another breakdown. During a round of Liz's routine bloodwork and scans, a radiologist noted a mass on her heart. It was small, but there was no mistaking it on her scan. We were referred to a heart specialist for a closer look. And this wasn't the only bit of concerning news we were facing. We were also getting news from another specialist about possible liver distress.

"*Oh God ...*"

I could feel the pressure tightening like a vice on my insides. I emailed my law partners to let them know that while we didn't know anything for certain, we were bracing ourselves for whatever came next.

It turned out, praise God, that the mass on her heart wasn't cancer. It is a rare (and entirely unrelated) condition that will require ongoing monitoring with the possibility of an eventual surgery to remove it. But no chemotherapy and no racing back to prep for another surgery—or at least not in the near future, anyway.

It felt like we had dodged a major bullet. But not exactly great news, either.

Because this all happened during COVID, we got our diagnosis over a zoom call with the heart specialist. The second that call ended, Liz and I once again collapsed to the floor, only this time we were in our basement instead of in the living room. It was a messy mix of relief and sorrow. Adrenaline overload, too. My mind was all over the place.

This is what passes for good news these days. I could feel the riptide dragging me out into the deep waters. I thrashed about.

After a few weeks of both of us struggling to re-stabilize, Liz offered a suggestion. "You need a support group," she said. "It's great that you are talking to a therapist, but I think you also need to talk to people who can relate to what we are going through."

This felt like a great idea and so I set out to find a group for caregivers. The tricky part was figuring out what I needed, exactly. Liz discouraged me from seeking a cancer-specific support group, which at first struck me as odd, but after talking through it with her made perfect sense. "There's going to be too many awful stories of people suffering and dying," she said. "That's the last thing you need to be surrounding yourself with right now." She was right.

But what, then? I did some internet sleuthing and found lots of different groups out there—bereavement groups, groups for caregivers of elderly patients, along with all kinds of cancer-related groups—but nothing felt quite right. I was dejected.

After stewing on this for a few weeks, I had an idea. I composed an email to the Rabbi, with the subject line "reaching out for advice." I wrote:

Hi Rabbi Berg,

I hope you and the family are well and that things are returning to as "normal" as normal can be these days.

I know this is a busy time of the year with the return to school and the High Holidays around the corner, but I am in need of a little help and could maybe use a nudge in the right direction.

The good news for the Ames crew is that our boys are great, our marriage is terrific, and Liz's health is mostly stable for the time being. But there's the rub: I say "mostly" stable because while her quarterly scans have all been clear since her chemo concluded last summer, there have been other issues with her liver and her heart that are also requiring monitoring. This has caused a great deal of stress, and while it ebbs and flows, our anxiety level is overall pretty high. There is this bracing for bad news that seems ever present in our lives, and while we've perhaps done a decent-seeming job from the outside looking in at managing all of this with joy, I'd be lying if I said any of this was easy.

And because there is the constant (and obviously understandable) focus on Liz and her well-being, I have moments of feeling a bit lonely and overwhelmed.

I've been seeing a therapist and have also been doing some reading, but it's dawned on me lately that I may not have all of the tools to help me on my journey as a caregiver. I'm wondering if there are support-groups for caregivers that you are familiar with? I spent some time on the Temple website today but didn't see anything that looked like it covered this. Obviously I can do my own internet exploring–and I have surfed around a little today–but I'd feel a lot more comfortable if it was someone you (or Rabbi Lapidus or Medwin) could vouch for. I'd prefer Jewish-based if such a thing exists but am open to anything.

I'm sorry to drop all of this on you but I've finally reached a point where I need to do something. Thank you, as always, for everything you do.

My very best,

Matt

The Rabbi is a pretty busy guy, but he called within minutes of me clicking send. We talked for several minutes as I filled him in on everything that was happening. He wasn't aware of a support group per se that checked all the boxes on what I thought I was looking for, but he did have an interesting idea. There was another young congregant at our synagogue he thought I might benefit from talking to. He connected us over email.

I don't feel comfortable using this book to share someone else's personal family details, so I am not going to use this person's real name (let's go with "Mark" instead), and I am also going to be purposefully vague about his backstory. But the Rabbi was on to something with this connection. Mark's story and family circumstances are different than Liz's and mine in many respects. Among other things, their journey does not involve cancer, but there is some definite common ground. We are both lawyers, we both have a household with two kids (and the same ages, at that), and we both know the unique stresses and pressures of being a caregiver. I'm sure the Rabbi's thinking was, *maybe these guys can lean on each other a little*.

Mark and I met for dinner a few days after the Rabbi connected us over email and we now get together often to share thoughts, advice, and words of support.

This connection has become deeply meaningful to me. On top of being a terrific guy, Mark has provided a much-needed safe outlet for me think out loud and be real with everything I've felt the past few years. It is therapeutic to do this with someone who relates in the way that he can. And I've learned a lot, too, because Mark is a few years further along on his journey than I am. He has shared insights and encouragement that only someone in the shoes of a caregiver could provide.

It's nice to know I'm not alone in feeling the way I feel.

When I first started talking about the idea of this book, one of the very first things Liz suggested was to include the unfolding of the events that led me to my friendship with Mark. Once again, I think she was right about that. It's been such an important part of the journey.

As Liz says, "Sometimes a caregiver needs support, too." I reached out for help and I am glad I did.

Wait! There's Some Good News, Too!

So now that we've dug through some of the tougher parts about being real with the feels, I want to re-frame this discussion and end on a high note. Because while keeping it real can connect you to some hard stuff, there's a real beauty embedded in all of this, too.

For one thing, there is value to being in touch with what's happening on the inside, caregiver or not. Of course it can be uncomfortable to go to that deep place we usually all work so hard to keep buried, but it also leads to some incredible insights, too. Yeah, this journey has tested me, but I now have a much clearer vision of what works for me and what doesn't. I'm better at anticipating stress triggers and better able to cope with the difficult moments. Knowing yourself better is valuable regardless of life circumstance.

And since you only get one chance at your life, you may as well do it in a way that's true to you. The time that you spend avoiding hard feelings is time you never get back, and avoidance rarely leads to emotional health in the long run anyway.

If that means sometimes acknowledging you are frightened or sad, own it. You may learn some things about your internal hardwiring just by being honest with yourself, and hopefully come out better on the other side when the moment has passed.

This last part is especially important. In order to get yourself comfortable with the idea of confronting that hard stuff, you must have faith that it will clear the path for better days ahead. Being real with the feels is not about collapsing into a state of resignation every time a negative feeling surfaces. Or acquiescing to a permanent state of stress or unhappiness. Rather, it is about being realistic with the fact that life is sometimes painful. Owning those moments—but with an eye towards better days ahead—is a way to cope and move on.

This is where counseling and being kind to yourself pays off. It's the old "daylight is the best disinfectant" kind of thing. And the bonus is that opening yourself up in this way enhances your sensation of the upswings in life, too.

Early on in her journey, Liz was told by another survivor that cancer can have an amazing tendency to make families love harder and see far greater beauty in everyday things. We were too frightened at the time to appreciate this wisdom, but the observation ended up being dead-on for us. Being real with the feels opens you up in all sorts of exhilarating ways. Having your sensors turned up high makes you appreciate things more.

Take music, for example. I've always been into it. I had a massive collection of CDs when I was a teenager and I've been to hundreds of concerts over the years. It's a part of me that goes way back.

But these days, it's so much *more*. I used to connect with it in a more detached kind of way. I mean, who doesn't like a good banger while heading out to the gym? But now I'm far more attuned to the beauty of a melody or the meaning behind the lyrics. When something speaks to Liz and me or seems to touch our circumstances in a direct way (two examples are *Beautiful Day* by U2 or *I'm Still Standing* by Sir Elton John), it elicits a visceral reaction. I hear and process the music in a different, deeper way.

My soul *stirs*.

Now transpose these sensory enhancements across other life experiences and you'll get the idea. Music is just one example of this phenomenon. My increased capacity for being touched by something beautiful extends far and wide. Weddings. An inspiring sermon by the Rabbi. Stories by other survivors. Things that used to just pass me by now sit with me longer. Same with Liz. We process things with bigger emotions, and without being self-conscious or apologetic about it. This adds texture and richness to our lives.

This kind of emotional transparency has also paved the way for a more authentic line of communication between us. Which allows for intimacy on a whole 'nother level. Because you can't claim to be soulmates with your partner without doing some soul-baring, right?

And while this kind of raw vulnerability can be awkward at times—yes, even after more than a decade of marriage and all that we've been through—the benefits are next-level. As with most things, you get out of your relationships what you put into them. Making a leap in the intimacy department is its own reward. Our bond is stronger than ever.

There's an everyday pragmatic reward to this approach with Liz, too. By being honest about our anxiety levels or moods on a particular day, we can both get more of what we are looking for and also be more responsive to the other person's current needs. This feels good in both directions. I enjoy not having to guess at Liz's mood or anxiety level on a given day, and I also appreciate that she makes a genuine effort to be sensitive to how I am feeling. It's a two-way street that reduces relationship traffic. It helps us avert potential arguments about who's in a bad mood or who's being snippy or who's overreacting or whatever. Think about it: how many times have you reflected on some big blowup with a loved one and realized it was mostly just because someone was in a bad headspace at that moment?

I'm not saying every argument can be traced back to anxiety or bad moods, of course. But at least some of them can, so those arguments can (hopefully) be avoided if everyone is transparent and honest about how they are feeling.

The most obvious example of this two-way street principle at work is the lead-up up to Liz's next round of bloodwork and scans. We're usually both on edge during this time, whether or not we express the angst. It is a lingering emotional residue from everything we've been through. Plus, the stakes are obviously high. So we're extra careful with one another during this time. We both give and receive extra grace.

But honestly, there doesn't even have to be a specific trigger or reason for whatever is going on internally. It's just a shared acknowledgment that we've been through an immense trauma together and that there are going to be reverberations from time to time that impact our moods. We don't have to rationalize or justify anything. We just share how we are feeling and provide comfort to one another.

***

Take care of yourself, friends. Do it for your loved ones who depend on you. Do it for you.

Chapter 14
Simplifying Your Life

The Urgency of Time

SHORTLY AFTER LIZ AND I got married and returned from our honeymoon, we went straight to an evening course at Emory University on financial planning. On the surface, this probably seems like the biggest buzzkill in the world, but for us it was just an extension of the honeymoon afterglow. Since we had spent much of our honeymoon discussing our plans of retiring young and traveling, this course seemed like a necessary first step toward that goal.

At the conclusion of the course, they gave us a free session with one of the instructors, Bill, who also had a private practice as a certified financial planner. I remember bringing a ton of paperwork with us and answering what seemed like a hundred personal questions, everything from our hobbies to how often we exercised. He took all of that information along with our pertinent financial data—our salaries, savings, retirement investments, everything—and said he would devise a plan to help us reach our life goals.

A few weeks later, we met with Bill again to go over our plan. He presented us with a thick binder filled with several pages of data and spreadsheets. We flipped through it. It had income and investment projections that ran forward decades. It looked like serious business.

Before we dove into the specifics, however, Bill had some big-picture advice for us. "You guys are doing great. You have steady jobs, you spend cautiously, and you save aggressively. I don't want to undersell the importance of investment strategy, but the most important asset you two have is your time. That's what you should focus on—how to allocate your time so that you are living in a way that is right for you."

Bill's advice resonated with me. It's an easy message to lose sight of in the daily grind. You get started with your career, you gain a little momentum, and it can be easy to switch over to auto-pilot. We focus on our career goals and milestones—along with all the obligations on our over-cluttered calendars—without hitting the pause button nearly often enough to ask, "Am I doing this in a way that's most meaningful to me?"

***

A few years after Liz and I had our meeting with Bill, I got another dose of this perspective in the unlikeliest of settings. It was during business pitch.

For context: when Eli was about a year old, I went out to California for work. I had a pair of client dinners to attend, and I also arranged for brief introductory meetings with a couple of client prospects. Basically, a networking and business development trip.

One of the prospects was the CEO of a prominent development company (let's go with "Saul" on this one). He was the consummate American success story: an immigrant who came to the United States as a young adult with nothing but the clothes on his back, but by a few decades later had amassed a substantial fortune in real estate holdings. A guy who had reached the upper echelon of professional success. A titan in the industry.

When I arrived for my meeting, I sat in the reception area for a few minutes and was then escorted into a large office where Saul greeted me. Our meeting was arranged via a close personal mutual connection, so there was an immediate warmth between us that is probably atypical for a first introduction in a business setting. After a few minutes of small-talk, we pivoted to a surprisingly heavy exchange:

"So, Matt. I hear you are a new Dad. How's it going?"

"It's a pretty big adjustment, of course, but we are all doing great. He's a really sweet little guy."

"You making it home in time for dinner and getting to spend enough time with him?"

"Most nights, yes."

"Good. Really important that you do that."

Of all the things I expected to talk about going in to this meeting, Saul's non-feigned interest in my work-life balance and in how much time I was making for my son was not high on the list.

But what surprised me even more was the story he told me next about his daughter, who was now in her mid-twenties. Saul told me that when she graduated from high school and went off to college in Texas, he went along to help move her in to her dorm, unpack, and get settled. At the end of that weekend, Saul got back on his two-hour return flight... and cried the entire way back home. And not just the sweet usual tears of a parent sending their kid off to college. These were tears of regret, lamenting the loss of missed years.

It turns out that when Saul was starting his family, he was so focused on growing his business that he missed out on everything else happening in his life. The late nights and work travel and weekends in the office came at the expense of celebrating all the little moments and milestones with his daughter. As he was returning from Texas to his home to California, he realized despite all his wealth and professional success, he had missed out on something precious—and something he could never get back. Those years were behind him before he ever got the chance to soak up the joy of being her dad. By the time he awakened to that fact, she was off to a faraway city.

I think about this exchange all the time. I had flown across the country to network and maybe develop a few business opportunities, and instead I came back with a jolt of perspective that has framed my life ever since: *Use your time wisely. It all goes by way too fast.*

Being Clear About Needs and Priorities

I took Saul's advice to heart, and by the time Isaac was born a couple of years later, I had done a decent job of streamlining things. I still put in my hours at the office, but just about everything else got scaled back: the happy hours to catch up with old friends, the non-essential networking stuff, and lots and lots of other little time-wasters that can eat into your week if you're not vigilant.

By no means did I have all the answers or always get it right, but I felt like I was succeeding more often than not in keeping the right balance. I was home for dinner most nights and, more importantly, had enough time and presence to play an active role in my boys' lives.

And then... July 2, 2019.

Since that phone call, the concept of time as a precious commodity transitioned from "point of measured emphasis" in our lives to a priority of the highest order. Because—not to be too overwrought about it—we still don't know what the future holds for us.

Of course, we are encouraged by how far we have come. But we also know how quickly all of it can change. While it's true that nobody knows for certain what tomorrow might bring, the instability of Liz's situation is far more than an abstract or hypothetical worry. It is an everyday existential threat, lurking.

So we strive to live with a laser sharp focus on making everything count.

But here's the tricky part. Living with this kind of urgency and focus is not easy. Talking about "the urgency of time" sounds great in theory. As a soundbite on Instagram, it's heartwarming as all get out. But it's hardly glamorous in practice. Pinning down that urgency in your day-to-day life requires tough choices and clear-eyed sacrifices. Because we still have lives to live, expenses to manage, and two young boys to raise.

Or, as Liz sometimes puts it, "shit still needs to get done."

This point bears emphasizing, because we've all heard some variation of this idealized theme of "living every day like it's your last." I wasn't a huge fan of that expression before July 2, 2019, and it has become especially problematic to me now. I know it's not meant to be taken literally, but it still has a foolish, unrealistic connotation that undersells the necessity of getting stuff done even under difficult circumstances.

I mean, would anyone still pay their monthly bills if they lived under this mantra? Or prioritize healthy lifestyle habits? Or invest in anything that didn't lead to immediate gratification? Yeah, I appreciate the sentiment of wanting to live with adventure and to not delay gratification, but living with the urgency of time is not a license to be reckless. Doubly so if you are responsible for the care of others, whether as a parent or caregiver.

So, how to balance it all? It is an ongoing task, but for Liz and me, living with urgency means forcing ourselves to be crystal clear about our needs and priorities, and then making intentional choices in service of those priorities. That's it—just the aim of being clear and living with intention.

I recognize I'm still trading in abstractions with this last part. Because "living with intention" might also be one of those expressions that has become popularized without any real substance behind it. It has a decent enough ring, but it can still be empty if not propped up with substance. And so here we go with that.

To us, the first step of living with intention is carefully distinguishing between *needs* and *wants*. This can be a deceptively tricky task, because while we all know the literal differences, in everyday practice these two concepts can easily get blurred.

Sure, we can all readily identify our most basic needs—food and shelter and such. But I contend the trap most of us fall into is stacking into the "need" column an awful lot of things that aren't really needs at all. Then we end up feeling frayed and overextended because our daily list of "needs" becomes impossibly long.

For example, how many times have you heard someone say that they are dreading some upcoming event that they "have to" go to out of a sense of social obligation? Or how many times have you yourself said that? That party you've been invited to—an event you have zero interest in attending—but that you feel compelled to attend because so-and-so might be there or because the host did XYZ for you however many years back or whatever it is? We sometimes say we "have" to go these kinds of things, but of course we don't actually "have" to in the literal sense. We always have the choice. Or, as one of our neighbors is fond of saying, "an invitation is not a subpoena."

Sometimes that choice comes at a cost. Actually, I'll rephrase that. That choice *always* comes at a cost. Because remember, time is our most precious commodity, and there is only so much of it we get. So if you choose to go to that social event you were dreading—and even if you somehow end up enjoying it—there was still a cost and a trade-off.

This is always so, even if the cost may not appear to be a major one at the moment. For me, the cost might be missing out on a night kicking the soccer ball in the backyard with my boys. Or the cost of staying up too late and having to drag myself out of bed the next day. Or missing an after-work run or bike ride. Or doing something else just for me. Confusing a "have to" for a "choose to" misallocates time that I will never get back.

Now look, I'm not saying people should say "no" to everything in life that isn't an absolute necessity. Not saying that at all. We all want to maintain friendships and stay connected to the outside world.

What I am saying, though, is that there is a tendency to get sucked into thinking we "have" to say yes to all kinds of things without giving enough thought to the cost that it imposes on us—even if only on our time. We do ourselves a disservice by failing to account for this.

To be fair, I suppose you could shrug your shoulders and say "so what" if we're just talking about one event in isolation. And I'll stipulate that it's not the end of the world to endure one night of suffering through an event you weren't super excited about but went to anyway. But it's never really just that one thing, is it? People who view everything as a "*have to*" instead of a "*choose to*" end up over-scheduled and lamenting the fact they don't have enough free time. That sensation of not having enough time ultimately leads to exhaustion and anxiety. And it all snowballs from there.

Liz and I know this phenomenon firsthand, because that was once our lives. For sure, it was how we lived before Eli was born. Even with the arrival of Isaac and the additional wisdom and perspective we picked up along the way (like the prescient advice I received from Saul out in California), we still often struggled to find the right balance.

This was a recurring theme in our lives—like it is with many young professionals—all the way up to the morning of July 2, 2019. Things got real clear to us real fast then. Among the millions of other little realizations that came crashing over us, we finally understood that the list of legitimate "have to's" in our lives was much shorter than our actions and choices were reflecting. Although it was a situation borne of good intentions, our lives were needlessly cluttered and complicated.

So, back to the "clear and intentional" part. As Liz regained her health and strength and as the world started opening up from COVID, we rethought our approach. Talking things through with an added focus to the "cost" side of the daily ledger has been a game-changer for us.

Yes, we still go out with friends and to concerts and other social engagements. But long gone are the days where we say yes to invitations to these kinds of things simply because we "have to."

Because we know we don't. And, in service of Saul's advice and in maintaining our sanity, we'll even say "no" to things that sound like fun once we feel like we're sliding into old bad habits. In short, we think long and hard before putting things on our calendar, as if every commitment of time were a major decision. Because it is.

This approach doesn't apply only to social engagements. It can be anything that is a drain on our time and emotional well-being. We talk about these little hidden costs all the time, and we weigh carefully whether they justify the trade.

Here's a random, recent example to illustrate the point: family holiday cards. We've been doing them every fall for years, and even managed to get one out a few weeks before Liz's surgery. But, as much as we enjoy sending them out, they take a lot of time and work. First, you have to schedule your family pictures. Then choose outfits and do the actual shoot. Then pick the one perfect picture that best captures the mood of the year out of the zillions they send you. Then come up with just the right message and design your card. Then update your mailing list, order the cards, stuff the envelopes, and apply the stamps. Then, *finally*, drop the things in the mail. We get a lot of satisfaction from sending and receiving them, but it's hours and hours of work. That's a real cost in terms of time, money, and headspace.

So this year, after discussing how we felt about it and considering everything else we had going on, we decided to forgo the cards. It had just become too much of our time and energy to feel good about. And although this was very much an annual family ritual for us, we were not going to make the mistake of treating the task as a "have to" and then make ourselves crazy trying to execute. We knew it was a "choose to." This year, we chose not to.

Now, again, I'm not saying people shouldn't invest the time to send holiday cards. Heck, I'm sure we'll get back to them again at some point. My point is we weren't going to fall into the old trap of treating this kind of thing as a "have to." Because that kind of thinking is a slippery slope leading nowhere good.

Language matters, and this little refinement in our day-to-day living has paid big dividends. Now, when Liz and I map out our upcoming week, we are far more precise about distinguishing "needs" versus "wants." We'll also look at whatever else we have going the week before and after to make sure we're not over-scheduling ourselves in service of any pressures that don't feel right to us. Now, when we sign up to do something that doesn't count as a "need," it's almost always because we really, genuinely want to, not because we tell ourselves, falsely, that we "have to."

Your time is precious. Treat it that way.

Prioritize Your Wants and Mind the Gap

Alright, so now I am going to backtrack and muddy the waters a bit. Notwithstanding everything I just said about distinguishing "needs" versus "wants," I'll concede there is a murky area within this binary paradigm to account for. It consists of those things in your life that maybe aren't *needs* in the literal sense, but they also don't quite fit into the *wants* category, either. We'll call this tiny space between the boundaries of *needs* and *wants* the Gap. And it is an important little space, even if you aren't a caregiver.

The big example for me is exercise, for all the reasons I got into before. It may not be a "need" in the same way that nourishment and sleep are, but it also exceeds my mere *wanting*. This was true for me in normal times, and it was especially true during the darkest days of Liz's journey, when I needed energy, balance, and a clear mind to power through. It was more than a "want," and so close to a "need" that I prioritized it just as if it were one.

That's the takeaway here. It pays to prioritize the things in the Gap, even if it requires careful planning and some sacrifice to make it happen.

The trick here is zeroing in on that *one or two things* you just can't do without. For many, this is no easy task, especially if you are an active, social person with lots of hobbies and interests. But this is why it is so important to be clear about priorities, because if you try to pull too many things from the Gap into your "needs," you'll never have the space to take care of everything else that needs tending to. Again, only so much time in the day.

While I would argue that regular exercise should fall into this bucket (and most health care professionals would probably agree), I recognize that for others, the idea of a workout regimen sounds more like drudgery than escape. I get that. The point I am getting at ties into the discussion above, about the importance of self-care, whatever that means for you. Your Gap may include playing an instrument, walking your dog, meditating, whatever it is. Whatever you pull into your "needs," you've got to make the time to do it.

Finding the Time

By interesting happenstance, this is a topic I have been talking about professionally for many years. Even before Liz's diagnosis, I have presented at college and law school events about the importance of maintaining a healthy life balance as a young lawyer, particularly about finding the time to pursue outside interests. It is an easy lesson to lose sight of, because law is a high-stress profession that can impose inordinate demands on time. Stress and burnout are endemic within the profession.

So I would go to these events and speak about keeping it all in perspective. Yes, starting your career off on the right foot is important, but not at the expense of losing sight of all the other things in life that keep us happy and healthy and balanced. I'd tell students they were people with outside passions and interests first, and future lawyers second.

My go-to closing remark: "Don't stop playing the guitar if that's your thing."

During these events, I'll inevitably get asked how to find the time to do all this when time as a lawyer is so scarce. I'll concede it's not an easy thing. It was difficult for me even before Liz was diagnosed. But there are a few life hacks I suggest that have served me well, both as a lawyer (though not so young anymore) and as a caregiver.

Once again, step one is clarifying priorities. I often tell students that while they may not find the time to do *everything* they enjoy doing on a regular basis, they can always find the time to do the most important stuff if they are deliberate and tactical about it. Just acknowledge and accept going in that no one in the history of the world has found the time to do it all.

Once you've built your list of priorities, the next step is identifying all the time-wasters. That's where you've got room to cut.

A big time-waster for me when our family was in the throes of our crisis was the evening news. As a lifelong news and political junkie, this was not an easy change. But it was a necessary one, because I was spending hours and hours a week in front of the television and consuming the news online after the kids were in bed. Once Liz was diagnosed, news consumption no longer seemed like a great allocation of my time, especially considering how toxic the news cycle has become. Old habits aside, I quickly realized this was an area where I had to trim back.

Another example that probably resonates with many: social media. What a problem that habit had become. I was wasting so much time—daily—mindlessly doom-scrolling through Facebook. And I'll admit I sometimes still do. But I've largely scaled the scrolling way back.

And then, of course, there's the earlier point about no longer giving time to things out of a sense of social pressure. Life's way too short.

It's amazing how much time cutting just those three things reclaims for me.

Those are the biggest examples, but there are many other things that have fallen by the wayside these past few years. Frankly, it's just your basic process of elimination. Over the course of a given week, by the time I have handled the "have to's" (work, time with Liz and the kids, sleep) and squeezed in the exercise, there's usually not much time left for other things. The extracurricular stuff I choose to invest my time in—occasional dinners with friends, going to a concert or sporting event, that type of thing—I plan weeks in advance. We give lots of thought these days to what goes on the calendar, and we say "no" far more often than we ever used to. Yeah, I miss out on some stuff, but rarely do I feel like I miss out on anything that matters in the big picture.

A final hack that may elicit some groans. For the past year or so, I've taken up the habit of getting up early most mornings.

Seriously early. As in, like, 4:15AM early. I know this may sound insane, but stay with me for a second.

With time being such a precious commodity, one way to capture a little more is to wake up earlier than normal and put the found (reclaimed) time to good use. While it takes some getting used to, the upside has been well worth the trade.

And it's not just the added time, although that alone is great. The early morning routine also reduces stress because I get to do things at my pace. My boys get up at 6:30 during the school year, and most days I drop them off and head to work. In order to do that, I need to be up and dressed before I wake them up so I can make them breakfast and ride herd over the morning routine. If I shot out of bed and sprinted through my own routine (a little caffeine, letting the dogs out, showering, getting dressed), the latest I could get up is 6am.

Except I don't want to start my day at a full sprint. I did things that way for years, and I've found that if you jump out of bed in a harried state, it impacts your mood for the rest of the day. Today, I'd much rather ease into the day at a relaxed pace, with the stillness of morning as my backdrop. And so I get up at that baffling hour and flow into my day with whatever I am in the mood for. Some days, that's reading for a few minutes. Other days, it's light stretching and some time on the stationary bike in our basement. A lot of days, I set aside 15-20 of those minutes to work on this book. Sometimes, I find myself with the time to do a little of all the above.

The funny thing is, now that I'm used to the routine, getting up this early doesn't feel like torture. It feels like an indulgence. All of this unhurried time to enjoy the quiet of the morning and do things how I want to. Often, those are the only moments of my week I'll get to savor.

***

Years ago, when I was first starting my law practice, a client gave me a gift. It was a little framed piece of art by an artist named Brian Andreas. I had never heard of him. The piece features a penciled sketch of a human figure, and beside the figure, this short inscription: *Everything changed the day he figured out there was exactly enough time for the important things in his life.*

This artwork has followed me through three moves over the past twenty-plus years, and I always have it displayed somewhere in my home. It looks nice, and I appreciated the gesture. But it is only during the past few years that its true wisdom and beauty sunk in.

I may not have time for everything these days, but I do have time for the things that matter. I'm thankful this thoughtful little gift had the patience for me to finally come around. One of life's great lessons had been right under my nose all along.

Set Boundaries

Okay. Let's say you've succeeded in prioritizing your wants and needs. The next hard step is setting boundaries and actually passing on things, because life has a way of moving along with all its deadlines and entanglements, whether or not you are up for it. Basically, you need to get comfortable with saying "no." Not just to social engagements, but to personal entreaties and other things that make demands on your time.

For me, this has been one of the more difficult parts of our journey. Prior to Liz's diagnosis, I already had in place some reasonably good life habits that continue to serve me well: exercise, practicing thankfulness, and faith. Sure, I've had to be intentional and deploy some discipline and resolve to get the most bang for the buck out of these things, but when Liz was diagnosed, I already had a sturdy foundation.

But when it came to setting boundaries? Let's just say I had a lot of work to do.

Although I don't want to get bogged down in why this is such a challenge for me, some high-level context may be helpful, if only because boundary setting seems like a common struggle for many people. So if we're speaking the same language here, just know there *is* hope. Because if I can make headway with this, anyone can.

The biggest thing for me is that I'm a pleaser. I fear triggering disappointment in others. For far too long—hell, decades—I found myself saying "yes" or just rolling with things when deep down I knew they weren't serving me.

Some of this may be cultural. You know, the whole "Jewish guilt" thing. But regardless of the origins, the uncomfortable weight of being a pleaser has been on my shoulders for as long as I can remember. The burden becomes doubly unhealthy when you're a caregiver. But everyone needs to be able to dig in their heels and say "no" sometimes. I'm sure there are a million ways you can slice and dice the idea of boundary setting, but I find it helpful to think in terms of two basic categories: boundary setting with life demands, and boundary setting with people.

Boundary setting with life demands was the easier part. This year's holiday card, for example. Once it felt like it was becoming too great a burden, we said "pass." Similarly, we started bypassing the need to over-orchestrate our boys' birthday parties. Released the pressure to make an entire production out of every time we have guests over. In almost every setting, we've taken to simple over complicated, and shed ourselves of the need for everything in our lives to appear buttoned up and perfect.

The people part, though, was not so easy. In fact, this is the most difficult of all the behavioral changes I have made since Liz's diagnosis. Because while projects don't get hurt feelings, people obviously do. And sometimes—not always, but definitely sometimes—they will let you know about it. But if the situation calls for it—and your gut will usually tell you when it does—you've got to swallow hard and take action.

So what do I mean by this? While people are layered and complex, it comes down to a pretty simple question: *Am I feeling good about the dynamics of this relationship as it currently stands?* If the answer to that question is "no," then the next step—and here comes the hard part—is taking action.

Sometimes this can take the form of tactful avoidance. I guess the modern term for this is "ghosting," but that sounds too melodramatic. I'm not talking about permanently swearing off friendships. But I do have far less time or inclination these days to keep up with high-maintenance relationships or relationships that don't feel right. I just allow the relationship to wither away in a polite and non-confrontational way.

Unfortunately, that passive approach doesn't always work. Sometimes, someone is too close to the center of your orbit to tactfully disengage without explanation. In those instances, "taking action" means being more direct and letting that person know that while you may still love them, you cannot—out of service to your headspace and well-being—abide by the status quo. The next step is to be really specific about your needs and your limits. Setting boundaries can—and often must—include having these difficult conversations.

Like I said, this has not been the easiest part of the journey for Liz and me. We've both had some tough conversations over these past few years with people we love. But if you subscribe to the idea that time is a precious and urgent commodity (which we do), and that taking care of yourself is top priority (which we also do), then healthy boundary setting is a must. Sometimes the uncomfortable call is the only option. You'll be better off in the end.

Lean Into Your Support System, Caregiver

This section comes about as the result of a great suggestion from Liz. After reading my first draft—hey, she loved it!—she issued a challenge of sorts: *Put yourself back in the early days of all of this and think about you needed. Share what you learned about the daily nuts and bolts. Caregivers need help and they need to know what to ask for. Same for people who have a caregiver in their lives and want to offer help but don't know where to start.*

I loved this idea. It makes all the practical sense in the world. And make no mistake: if you ever find yourself unexpectedly thrust into the role of caregiver, you're almost certainly going to need help. So here we go.

The first big thing was food. For many months, there wasn't time to plan trips to the grocery store or figure out meals for the week. But this problem was solved for us as soon as we shared our news. Just having a casserole or something else pre-made that we could pop into the oven or microwave was a huge time saver and stress reliever. As an aside, I think people enjoyed being able to help in this way, and there was never a shortage of volunteers to either bring us home-cooked meals or place orders for us online. We seriously had food lined up for almost an entire year.

The second thing was figuring out a team of family and close friends who could help with Eli and Isaac. I don't mean like a few hours of babysitting here and there. I mean people who were at the ready to roll up their sleeves and care for them while I was gone for extended stretches. There were days when I would take the boys to school in the morning and wouldn't see them again until early evening, after they had already been bathed and fed. While Liz was in the hospital and for several weeks after her return home, I had a group text going with people offering to care for the boys whenever we needed it. They coordinated pickups and drop-offs and kept Eli and Isaac happy and entertained while I was tending to Liz. Again, a huge help.

Admittedly, it wasn't easy to let go of the reins here. My protective parenting instinct was in hyper-drive, and I worried frequently about the boys feeling confused by all the abrupt changes to our family routines. Or, worse, feeling abandoned. Being away from those guys for long stretches was hard, especially when they were so young.

But I also knew I couldn't be in two places at once, and Liz needed me too. So at some point, you have to lean really hard on your inner circle and have faith that your kids are going to be cared for. Thankfully, ours were.

I cannot overstate the importance of this. Our boys have come through this saga pretty unscathed, all things considered. True, little kids can be more resilient than they get credit for. But I also believe all the hands-on care they received played a big part in their stability. Mom and Dad may not have always been around, but there was never an absence of love or comfort in their everyday lives. I'm glad I resisted my initial (and ill-advised) instinct to think I somehow could handle all their needs without major help.

This help extended to staying on top of our school and activity calendars. All the important dates—school holidays, parent-teacher conferences, social activities—were maintained for us via electronic calendar invites from other families. I never would have thought to ask for help in this area, but it ended up being a big assist. All I had to do was click "accept" and all of my appointments relating to the boys were laid out for me. Another huge time-saver and stress release. Because lord knows that's a lot to keep up with.

Finally, we got lots of help with weekly errands and household chores. Runs to and from the drugstore to pick up Liz's prescriptions. Vouchers for professional help with laundry and other household chores. Lots of other similar gestures. More precious time freed up for me to spend caring for Liz and the boys.

The old "it takes a village," right? If you're a caregiver and the offer for help is out there, don't be prideful. Don't overthink it. Accept it and be thankful for the grace.

Chapter 15
Practice Thankfulness

THERE IS A WONDERFUL, underrated movie from the early 2000s called *8 Mile*. It tells the tale of an aspiring rapper from Detroit trying to overcome all kinds of personal hardship and turmoil in pursuit of his dream to make it big. Eminem stars in the leading role, a gritty performer named B-Rabbit, and the movie reportedly involves semi-autobiographical elements of Eminem's early life.

If you've never seen the movie, it's worth a watch even if you aren't a fan of Eminem specifically or rap music generally. The story is not only deeply engaging, but simmers with social commentary about how chronic poverty plagues our big cities and the daily struggles people endure just to keep their heads above water.

Although the story is rife with substance abuse and violence, the cinematography manages to give a haunting beauty to the menacing edge. At the center of it all is B-Rabbit, who carries not only the weight of an addict mother, but also a neglected kid sister he desperately tries to comfort and protect, all while working a dead-end factory job. It is a lot of despair. All the while, he tries to scrape together enough free time and money to launch his budding music career.

At the risk of sharing spoilers for anyone who hasn't seen it but may now be curious, there is a rap battle scene at the end of the film where B-Rabbit finally takes center stage and finds his voice. And his message is triumphant.

Despite the challenges—the abject poverty, the toxic home life, the unrelenting violence and chaos in the community—he decides the only way to face his considerable demons is with head held high. He comes to this realization while delivering a stage performance with middle fingers on blast (this is a semi-auto biographical tale about Eminem, after all), but the lesson behind the moment is crystal clear: *I may have been dealt a bad hand, but I am not going to allow it to take my spirit.* Every time I catch this movie when I'm scrolling through the channels, I have to stay tuned through the end just to catch this final scene.

It's powerful stuff. And while I may be stretching a little with the takeaways of what the writers and director intended—I'm guessing this is the only book that's ever been written by a caregiver who attempts to draw tenuous *8 Mile* parallels—it is a mindset that I come by honestly. And I am glad that I do, because it has helped me find and embrace even the faintest of light during the darkest of moments.

Let me back up before expanding on this point. Long before Liz's diagnosis and everything that followed, the act of consciously expressing gratitude had already become a deeply engrained personal ritual. I can't pinpoint exactly when this became such a thing for me, but it probably started taking root when I graduated from law school and entered the workforce. I was a pretty idealistic bordering on naïve kid growing up, so it was eye-opening to leave the relatively sheltered environs of university life and enter the "real world." It didn't take long to realize how fortunate I was, and it felt important to me not to take that good fortune for granted. The power behind this idea of gratitude has expanded in my mind as I have gotten older.

One important early influence came from an older woman named Grace (*not using her real name*), who worked in our mail room when I was just starting out at my firm. She had a deep voice and a beaming smile. Every day she'd push her little cart around the office, drop off our individual pieces of mail, and stick around for a moment of small-talk. And every day as she came by with the mail, we would kick off our banter with the same exchange:

"Grace! How you doin' today?"

"Good morning, Matthew! And you know what? Every day above ground is a good day!"

This ritual became our little inside joke, and it went on for years. We could not engage in any other pleasantries until we got that scripted Q&A out of the way.

And then one day Grace was no longer around the office. This was an unexpected, out-of-the-blue development from my vantage point, and I learned of it literally by just looking up from my desk one morning and seeing someone other than Grace pushing the mail cart around. Because I was still in the "new guy keeping his head down" mode, I didn't ask any questions. All I knew was that my daily blast of sunshine and chit-chat was gone.

I don't recall ever being given a reason for her departure. This is not particularly remarkable to me in hindsight, because people come and go at law firms all the time. I assume she found another job and is now cheerfully blasting sunshine on other lucky co-workers. It has been close to twenty years since I last saw her, yet I still think of her often.

While Grace's unfailingly cheerful demeanor was memorable in its own right, what stands out to me now is an additional fact I learned about her a few years after she left the firm.

It turns out that behind her wide smile was a very troubled home life, which may or may not have involved a volatile marriage and suspected issues with addiction. Sadly, Grace had an awful lot weighing on her during the years she was proclaiming her gratitude just to be above ground.

And yet I don't think she was being insincere in expressing her gratitude. While it is obviously impossible to know for sure what is going on in someone else's mind, there was too much warmth behind those eyes—and too much unprompted laughter and too many acts of kindness—for this to have all been a contrivance. No way she could have faked it with such conviction for so many years if it wasn't really how she felt.

No, this was a person—just like B. Rabbit from *8 Mile*—who had apparently been dealt some pretty tough cards but was nonetheless determined to focus on the positives in her life, smile wide and head held high. Every day above ground for Grace was indeed a good day.

Grace's take on the world left quite an impression on me as a younger lawyer trying to figure out my way in the "real world," but it was by no means the only one. Because once you decide to be receptive to the stories playing out around you, good life lessons are everywhere to be found. So I took a lot of mental notes of those around me, like Grace, who were determined to live life with a focus on the positives regardless of circumstance. The path of gratitude seemed an enriching one to follow.

There were two other big influences that further cemented this type of thinking for me. The first was rooted in faith and spirituality. Obviously, that's a hefty topic in its own right—and one that

I dedicate the entire next chapter to—but a few thoughts are in order to connect the dots on the present point.

At the same time I was getting my bearings in the "real world" as a young professional, I was also trying to sort through my views on faith and the role it should play in my life. Like a lot of young American Jews, I had been exposed to many of the teachings and traditional indoctrination growing up. I had celebrated a Bar Mitzvah—the rite of passage when a Jewish child passes into adulthood in the eyes of the Jewish community—and certainly self-identified as a Jew culturally. But, to be totally honest, I also had a fair amount of skepticism about the whole organized religion thing, as well as unresolved questions about what I even believed. I carried these doubts and misgivings with me as I grew from adolescence into young adulthood.

Then you leave home and head off to college, at which point you're kind of left to decide what role, if any, your spirituality should play in your life as you stake out your place in the world.

But my skepticism and misgivings notwithstanding, I was curious enough as I was leaving law school to give it all more consideration. And so, once I moved up to Atlanta, I sought answers and additional perspectives. I signed up for adult education classes at a local synagogue. I joined a meditation group that focused on using Jewish mysticism as a pathway to inner peace (yes, seriously). I also befriended a few rabbis, who I would occasionally take to lunch to ask the *big* questions about life and death and everything in between. I still wasn't sure what I did or didn't believe, but I had a longing for spiritual meaning that I felt compelled to keep exploring. I was looking for something beyond simply self-identifying as Jewish.

Throughout this exploration, the idea of expressing gratitude kept resurfacing. I didn't know what was out there behind all the wonder and unknowns in the world, but I sure was thankful for it. And that became the connective tissue, if you will, between my faith and my feelings of gratitude. These two ideas—gratitude and spirituality—were nourishing each other and growing stronger inside me. *How were they interconnected?*

I know this will feel like a reach for some. Certainly, I get that one take on religion is that it's just a bunch of "thou shalls" and "thou shall nots," which sounds more like overbearing rules than thankfulness. But that's not how I was choosing to see it. Rather, I began to see faith as an incredible way to channel and express the gratitude I was already building as a philosophical pillar. So, as I leafed through Jewish literature and sat through evening lectures trying to get my spiritual bearings, I focused less on the idea of religion as a list of stern commandments and more on the idea of religion as a ritual and language to express thanks for the beauty and wonder of it all. Viewed through that lens, spiritual faith wasn't a limiting or oppressing concept for me. Instead, it was liberating.

Fortunately, these ideas resonated with Liz, too. Liz had little exposure to Judaism before we coupled up, but she knew it was a big part of who I was and she wanted to relate to me on that level once it became clear we were going to be building a family together. So in the early years of our relationship, Liz joined me on my spiritual path. She attended evening classes with me at the local synagogue. We read and talked about books. We became members at a synagogue, befriended the clergy, and asked lots of questions. We sought other interfaith couples to share our common thoughts and experiences. And from all of that, we decided we would create a spirituality in our home that wasn't based on ironclad rules, but on expressions of faith tethered to Jewish traditions and—most importantly—anchored in gratitude.

The best example of how we tied this all together is our family practice of Shabbat, the Jewish Sabbath. Shabbat is also known as the "day of rest," and it runs for the 24 hours following sundown on Friday evening. During that stretch that wraps up Saturday evening, the scriptures say that Jews are supposed to rest, pray, and enjoy quiet time together as a family.

The Friday night part of Shabbat traditionally involves a few rituals: the lighting of two candles to welcome in the Sabbath, the recitation of a couple of prayers, and then the Sabbath meal.

Basically, it's all a big ceremonial "thanks" to God for the occasion of a Friday evening together. Which, if you think about it, is a pretty cool concept, since the passing of another ordinary week can seem like a mundane thing unless you force yourself to stop, reflect, and express genuine thanks for it. "Every day above ground is a good day," anyone?

Since Liz and I were carving out our own family traditions anyway, we decided to reimagine Shabbat in a more personalized format. To us, it is so much more than just an opportunity to say the same few prayers each week, light some candles, and call it a wrap. That tradition-based ritual provides a nice backdrop, but we wanted our Shabbat practice to attempt a deeper dive into what it all means for us.

So, in our home, after we light the candles and recite the traditional prayers, we share a few thoughts of reflection. Everyone at the table takes a moment to say what they are thankful for that week. This includes our boys and any other guests or family who may join us.

The trip around the table usually only takes a moment or two, but they can be surprisingly intimate and humbling. Because while there are certainly some themes that get repeated over and over ("family," "soccer," and "weekend time together" tally a lot of votes these days), it is powerful stuff to have your spouse or child look you dead in the eye and tell you how thankful they are. And so, after everyone at the table has spoken, you take a breath, you exhale, and more often than not, a deep sense of contentment stirs inside you. *You know what? We're all here, we're together, and we have another week to look forward to.*

In my book, that's a *lot* to be thankful for.

I recognize it sounds a little strange to say I am thankful for being thankful, but I do believe that having this Shabbat ritual firmly in place by the time July 2, 2019, rolled around played a huge role in keeping our spirits lifted. We certainly weren't going to stop saying we were thankful once Liz was diagnosed, and so the weekly exercise forced us to direct our focus onto the positive. We had to be careful with our words around the boys, of course, but the underlying message was clear and it felt good for Liz and me to say certain things out loud, together: *We're thankful for our beautiful family. We are thankful for the memories we've made together. We are thankful for the world-class community at Emory. We are thankful that Mommy is a fighter.*

And yes, *we are thankful for God*. That's a big one, worthy of further exploration, because sometimes in the bleakest moment your faith is all you've got.

But before we switch over to that channel, I want to talk about the last big influence on our thankfulness mindset that has lifted us through the difficult times. This one, I will admit, was a simple stroke of fortune.

A couple of years before Liz was diagnosed, my father sent me a book he thought I would take to: *The Daily Stoic*, by Ryan Holiday and Stephen Hanselman. It's a series of short essays on the philosophy and teachings of stoicism. Dad's hunch was correct. I devoured the book and have passed it along to several others since. Indeed, *The Daily Stoi*c wasn't just a just a thoroughly enjoyable book, it became the recipe for the kind of life I wanted to live.

There's an awful lot to stoicism—way too much for me to cover in this book—but the grossly oversimplified version boils down to the notion that everything in life is ultimately how we choose to see it. According to the stoics, the only thing we can fully control in the chaotic and unpredictable world around us is our thoughts. Everything else—our health, our economic circumstances, the physical domain around us—can be changed or erased in an instant. At bottom, our thoughts are all we have.

This idea was the final, awesome piece for me. Because believing your thoughts are what matter most implies we always have a choice on how we will live, even when the chips are down. Our minds can create every kind of lens or filter; it is up to us to decide which ones we will ultimately use.

To me, this was an easy call. Regardless of circumstance, I would choose to build my life on gratitude and faith.

Then I did my best to walk the walk. And I'm here to tell you, sticking to it can change everything for the better if you let it. One morning a few months before Liz's diagnosis, I had an amusing lemons-to-lemonade moment I posted about on social media:

Funny start to the day today: as Eli and I were leaving the house for me to drop him off at school, Isaac—who was still in his slippers and pajamas—asked to come along for the ride. He makes this request from time to time and it typically isn't rather convenient, because (a) it means I have to take him back home after dropping Eli off instead of going straight to work; and (b) it's about a 2 block walk to Eli's school from where we park, and Isaac more often than not insists on being carried for this part of the trek and he's gotten to a size where doing this (in a suit, no less) is a bit more of a workout than you would choose for yourself while trying to hustle into the office without lathering into a second quarter sweat.

But I threw him in the car with Eli and me anyway and obliged, mainly because I was flattered by the request (unlike his adoring older brother, Isaac barely tolerates me about 50 percent of the time) and figured it was a good way for us to spend a few minutes of quality time together. And, being the last minute (but somehow highly functional) planner that I am, I even grabbed him a little rain jacket for good measure because he's been battling with the flu and it was cloudy and misty outside. Good thinking, Dad!

Naturally, by the time we pulled up to our friends' house for the 2 block walk, it was no longer misting but now completely pour-

ing—and while I did bring a jacket for Eli and Isaac, I emphatically did not bring one for myself. And while our dear friend Lauren did see me in my plight and offer me an umbrella to borrow for the walk, there was no avoiding the full on shower I was getting, wholly suited up, while hauling Isaac in my arms to and from the school.

But while I was walking back from school and straining under the weight of Isaac in my arms while getting absolutely dumped on by this surprise shower, all I could keep thinking is that I am the luckiest sunuvabitch alive. Yeah, getting drenched in your suit while carrying your Too-Heavy-to-be Carried-for-Two-Blocks toddler is certainly not ideal, but how lucky am I to have two incredible little boys who made this very moment of surprise rain possible? And a wife who leaves you breathless and in awe every day with her strength and her fire and her heart and her beauty? Bring it on, Surprise Rain Shower.

And especially this also—I'm thankful to you all—the friends and family (old and new, near and far) who thought of me today to wish me a happy birthday and poke a little fun at me for being one year older. I've always maintained that one of the great keys to happiness is to recognize your blessings, and you all are blessings of the highest order. So, from the bottom of my aging but still hopelessly idealistic heart, thank you, thank you, thank you. I am one fortunate dude.

February 6, 2019.

Obviously, I had no idea what was in store for us as a family when I wrote that. But I'm glad I was already in that kind of headspace when we got the news. Hopelessness and despair can take you to the bottom quickly. You'll sink fast if you don't stay in front of it.

Fortunately, I've been mostly able to stick with this mindset in my caregiver role, although it obviously hasn't always been easy. Staying thankful and positive takes real discipline and commitment, and sometimes the rope slips no matter how tightly you grip it.

This reality is a big part of why I go so deeply into the dark moments in Chapter 10, because I certainly wouldn't want to leave the impression that viewing everything through thankful lenses is just like a light switch that you can flick on and off. This stuff takes work, but the payoff sure is worth it. And, while I have fallen down hard a few times, the glass-half-full take is that my dedicated practice of thankfulness helped keep me from spiraling down even deeper in those difficult moments.

I'll close out this point with another tie-back to social media. This time a post from December 2021, just over two years after Liz's surgery:

Lots and lots to reflect on over the past year—bucket list trips, the joy of watching our boys grow up (albeit much too quickly), and a pretty terrific year professionally. I even completed my first Olympic distance triathlon this past September—the first race I had completed in years and the longest and most difficult by far.

And when I sat down to write this, I thought about going deep on all of these subjects. Lord knows I could string together several paragraphs on weekend soccer games alone. Imagine how many words I could spill over an entire year of travel and parenting adventures.

But when you cut all the way through it, it always comes down to this.

I'm the luckiest guy in the world. I acknowledge this every day. And I am thankful for every minute that we have together. The secret sauce for me is simple but potent.

Yup. Every day above ground is a good day. Choosing to see it that way has made all the difference.

An Important Note About Privilege

While this book focuses on our personal story and the lessons I've learned, it is impossible to paint a fair and complete picture without addressing the broader subject of privilege.

Undoubtedly, Liz possesses extraordinary spirit and determination, and her recovery probably would not have not been possible without those traits. But it is equally true we would not be where we are today without our access to first class health care services made possible by our employer-provided insurance.

In late December 2019, the mailman brought us some holiday cheer in the form of a statement for services rendered on November 6, 2019, the date of Liz's surgery. The sum total was just over $320,000 ($320,330.35 to be exact). That was for *one day* of medical treatment. While we have not tallied all the other charges along the way—the scans and blood draws, the biopsies, the chemotherapy, the genetics testing, and countless other hours we have spent in consultations and in receiving other forms of treatment—I'm certain that cost is easily in the millions.

Because we have employer-provided insurance, only a tiny fraction of this cost has fallen on our shoulders. But our relief of being spared that impossible burden aside, the empath in me cannot help but wonder where someone else in our situation would be without insurance.

Liz and I have been blessed with stable incomes for years and have done all the right things in terms of saving and living within our means and such, but without insurance we would have instantly exhausted our life savings and then been neck-deep in our crisis without medical help. Our medical bills are still in the thousands of dollars every year, and that's *with* insurance. Without it, no way we could have ever kept up. This already difficult situation would be catastrophic.

So I cannot do full service to our story without addressing the subject of privilege, and how much I struggle with the outsized role it plays in the determination of those who get quality treatment and those who do not.

So, fair warning, I am now going to preach for a couple of paragraphs. There is a popular narrative being told in certain political circles that health care is available to anyone willing to work for it, and that the people who argue for universal healthcare are enabling freeloaders. I have a really difficult time accepting this narrative. If we have learned anything at all about our economy in this generation—with our pandemics and Wall Street meltdowns—it is that job security is fragile even for the most industrious among us.

Think about it. All of us know someone who has lost a job or is between jobs. This is not because everyone who is out of work lacks a work ethic or an ability to "lift themselves up by their bootstraps." Many end up in that place because shit sometimes happens and because our economy, wonderful as it is in some respects, doesn't always do a terrific job of looking out for the less fortunate. And while I was fortunate enough to keep my job during this time, it's not that far-fetched to imagine a scenario where things played out differently for us. What if Liz had gotten sick during a time when I happened to be out of work at that moment? What if we didn't have employer-provided insurance? I spent hours and hours at Emory during the month of November staring out of our hospital room window, pondering all of this.

That's the tragic part about the current state of our health care system. It fails too many when they need it most. You lose your job—whether due to economic downturn or because you yourself are too sick to work—and your insurance goes away with it. And if you don't have other coverage immediately lined up (for example, a cancer-free spouse who is also on private insurance), you are in serious, serious trouble. Health care has become, frankly, a fickle luxury good.

I recognize this is an issue fraught with political disagreement, and I certainly do not have all the answers. But it is our moral imperative to address it in a meaningful way. I am eternally thankful for the treatment that Liz and I have received, but our fates should not be dictated solely because of fortunate timing and privilege. We can and should do better.

Thankfulness as an Everyday Practice

Soapbox stowed. Back to the everyday life stuff.

While thankfulness has been indispensable to my mindset as a caregiver, it's so much more than a crisis management tool. I'd argue it is one of the key distinguishing features between those who are content in life and those who are not, if not *the* distinguishing feature.

I know that can sound like words coming from a privileged place. I get that. And, to be sure, I have certainly enjoyed many of the vestiges of what most would consider a privileged life: a stable and solidly middle-class upbringing, with access to quality education and healthcare. There's a lot I never had to worry much about. At least not before everything that happened with Liz, anyway. It might be tempting to say it's easy for someone who has so much to feel contentment.

But Grace certainly proved that one can face a lot of hardship and still maintain a focus on the positive side. And don't forget what the stoics say: all of that external, circumstantial stuff can change in an instant anyway, for the good or the bad. That was certainly the case for Liz and me. Yet we still found our way back to gratitude. No, the vestiges of "privilege" alone can take you only so far.

Besides, think about all the people in your life who seemingly have everything one could wish for but still can't find true happiness. I have witnessed those sad examples over the years: folks who amass great wealth and professional success but still seem perpetually unfulfilled. Privilege may make life easier, but it by no means guarantees happiness.

And that is because so much of life is how we choose to see it. There's a reason "comparison is the thief of joy" is such a common expression. It's just another way of expressing the sentiment that if you're only focused on what you don't have, instead of on what you do, you'll never find true fulfillment. You have to be thankful for what you *do* have, whatever that may be.

I believe this with every fiber of my being. In fact, if you take nothing else away from this entire book, take that. Be thankful for what you have.

I have read a fair amount over the years about life lessons from the perspective of older adults, including a fascinating piece in the *New York Times* several years ago entitled *The Wisdom of the Aged*. There are many valuable nuggets if you go down the internet rabbit hole on this. Advice on everything from child rearing to travel to money management. But if you wade through the wide swath of advice on these subjects, a few key themes repeatedly come up: *Spend less time worrying. Let go of whatever bad feelings you are harboring. I wish my younger self had known these things.*

This may be my confirmation bias speaking, but I believe this is the essence of stoicism and gratitude. Excessive time spent worrying means less time available for being thankful. Time spent worrying is time you never get back. The same applies to any other type of resentment or bad feelings you are harboring. As I often like to say, no one lies on their death bed wishing they had spent more time during their life being pissed off.

So now it is part of my daily ritual. I challenge myself to say *thanks* every day, and not just say it, but *mean* it. *Every day above ground is a good day.*

As it relates to Liz, the thinking is simple. There is no path I could envision for myself in this world (and the next one, if you accept that kind of thing) that does not include her. So if being a caregiver to Liz is part of the gig, so be it. I happily, thankfully accept. And I treasure all our moments together, the good and the bad.

I am my Beloved's and my Beloved is mine.

I apply this to all the other things in our everyday lives, like parenting. Raising two active little boys is hard, and it can test your patience in all kinds of ways: the muddy footprints, the bickering, the constant griping about bedtime and homework. All the stuff. You can quickly get frustrated if you allow it.

Because let's face it, fellow parents: a lot of parenting is a grind. The diapers and the tantrums and the sleepless nights. The constant triangulating of your weekly schedule in service of other little people. The surrendering of so much of your personal interests and your free time. It can sometimes be a real drag. It's tempting to say, "I can't wait until this stage of life is behind us."

But here's the flipside. All those little moments go by and never come back.

Liz and I are in an odd little stage of our life these days, which involves both boys being hell-bent on sleeping on Mommy and Daddy's bedroom floor. We'll tuck them into their own beds and say goodnight, but then invariably a few hours later one or both of them will creep into our room and make a little pallet of blankets and pillows somewhere on our floor. It's less than ideal for all kinds of reasons, not the least of which is that it's a total trip hazard. On more than one occasion, I have gotten up in the middle of the night only to stumble over one of my perfect little angels sleeping peacefully right below my side of the bed.

Can this be a bit annoying? For sure. But am I wishing the moment away? Absolutely not.

Because one morning—and it will come with no warning or fanfare—I'll get up in the middle of the night, and my path to the bathroom or fridge will be clear. My not-so-little angels will be perfectly content in their own rooms. No pallets or pillows on the floor. No instinctive need for the comfort of Mom and Dad nearby in the middle of the night. That stage of life will be over. And I will miss it. I suspect a part of me will ache for it.

Takeaway? Stay present. Appreciate the moments for what they are.

I think this is part of what made Saul so sad. It wasn't just that he didn't spend wisely the time he had with his daughter. It was that he also failed to fully appreciate the little time he did spend with her. He wasn't present enough to create lasting memories. And before he knew it... the opportunities were gone.

So now, almost every time I feel my blood pressure starting to rise, I stop. I check myself. And I remind myself it wasn't all that long ago that I was lying awake at night wondering whether I'd be dealing with the muddy footprints, and the bickering, and the constant griping about bedtime and homework... all by myself. And what that devastation for the boys and me would have felt like.

With that, I've imprinted a lasting memory and flipped the moment of frustration on its head.

Thank God we are all here together to untangle a barbed fishing lure from the air conditioning ducts, after Isaac decided it was a grand idea to practice casting his new rod in our downstairs mechanical closet.

Thank God we are all here, huddled together as a family in front of the iPad, scanning the Google results of "how to safely remove permanent marker from child's face."

Thank God for the near-constant echo of a soccer ball *thump thump thumping* throughout the house while the boys argue over who was offsides and who gets a yellow card for dirty play and who gets to pretend to be Cristiano Ronaldo for their next indoor grudge match.

Thank God for the muddy footprints, the middle-of-night trip hazards, and for all the noise.

Thank God for my beautiful family. All of us, enjoying these precious moments in time together.

Chapter 16
Have Faith

Spoiler alert: I am not a religious scholar. Nor would I consider myself a particularly devout Jew. Still, though, faith has played an indispensable role in my journey. Actually, better to say, in *our* journey.

I reckon you've gleaned this by now. References to faith and God are everywhere in this book. But since it's such a big and important topic, I didn't want it to seem like it was merely a side-note to all the other ideas I've been unpacking. Quite to the contrary, faith is the foundation of everything for us. So, as thorny as the topic can be, I knew as I was writing this book that it needed its own separate discussion.

But first things first: how I got here. I hinted at this process earlier. As important as faith is, the pieces did not come together easily for me.

For starters, there's the whole organized religion thing. It's easy to find examples throughout history of people doing horrible things to one another in the name of religion. And it's not just a historical problem. Atrocities are still being committed in service of religious disagreements across the globe. If you want to argue—from a strictly utilitarian perspective—that organized religion has done more harm than good, I'm not here to stop you.

Here's the thing, though. I eventually got to a place where my big-picture misgivings about organized religion didn't automatically disprove the existence of "God." Basically, I've determined that two things can be true at once: we can both live in a world where God as a deity exists, but also where you still unfortunately have horrible people doing horrible things (ostensibly) in God's name.

After all, it is only when you define the idea of "God" as a concept that can exist only in the absence of suffering that you can use the fact of ever-present human suffering to disprove God's existence. My definition of God does not include this requirement, and the way I bridged that gap was through the concepts of agency and free will. If you decide that God gave people the gift of free will, then it will always be possible for them to cause harm in the name of religion.

But my skepticism about faith and God wasn't just rooted in mistrust for organized religion. Once I overcame that hurdle, the next question was: *Why*? Because after you the cut through all the dogma and rituals and other stuff, you still have the option to choose whether or not you believe. So, it's an entirely fair question I sometimes wrestle with. Why faith?

The short answer is: because it serves me really well. I just had to build my belief system in a way that made sense to me.

There are two pillars to this build-out. The first is that I've given myself the freedom to question. It's liberating, and I've found it is not incompatible with faith. Probably doesn't seem like traditional religious dogma to many, but for me it is a core tenet of my spirituality. Ironically, the foundation of this first pillar was poured during a discussion I was having with someone where I was making the case *against* organized religion.

Here's the backstory. I've used the word *journey* a lot symbolically here, but now I finally get to use it in the literal sense. Right after college, I took an actual journey overseas (with one of the aforementioned Broitmans from way back in Chapter 1), and our journey led us to, among other places, Israel.

While we were there in Israel, I met a student who was studying to become a Rabbi. He was not much older than I, and there was a certain approachability about him that made me feel comfortable asking all the big, hard questions. The kind of guy you have beers with. Which, for the record, we were, as I unknowingly approached my *a-ha!* moment.

Anyway, we talked about all kinds of things, but the most lasting exchange in my mind was when I asked him if he really believed that all the stories we had been taught in Hebrew School actually happened as described: the parting of the Red Sea as the Israelites were fleeing persecution, the delivery of the Torah to Moses on Mount Sinai, and all the other stories we were told as kids but that seem so highly improbable when you think about the physical attributes and limitations of the world around us. I went on and on, expressing my doubts. Surely all of this cannot be so, right?

The young Rabbinic student listened patiently as I delivered my long-winded exposition, and how these obvious man-made fictions caused me to struggle with the notion of any religion or religious dogma. Then, for good measure, I railed against organized religion, too. He nodded. He looked at me with kind eyes.

And then, when I finally stopped talking, he responded warmly and earnestly. "Matt, I hear you. I really do. But there is a difference between taking this all *seriously* versus taking it *literally*. Faith can be a beautiful thing. Don't get hung up on the literal. Give yourself room to question. And if you allow yourself to view it that way, there is an awful lot of wonderful stuff to explore."

That idea hit me hard. The freedom to explore my Jewishness on my terms? It was like a portal opened in my mind, just waiting for me to walk through.

Now, I'm not going to say this one exchange ended all the questions or uncertainties in my mind, because it didn't. That's kind of the whole point. And I'm likewise not going to suggest this exchange propelled me down the path of rigorous religious observance, because it didn't do that either. I was a skeptic with a largely secular lifestyle before this conversation with the young student and I remained so afterwards. In that sense, nothing changed.

But this conversation triggered a significant and lasting paradigm shift. Before, it had always seemed wrong to give my questions and skepticism room to breathe. Being told—by an aspiring Rabbi, no less—that skepticism was not just *allowed* but *encouraged* felt like a tremendous spiritual weight being lifted off my shoulders. I suddenly could look at things in a different way: *take things seriously but not literally.*

It was liberating to break through this spiritual logjam, because I've always had the inner belief there was something out there beyond my comprehension. And I've always had the urge to connect with that "thing" even if I couldn't fully (or even mostly) understand it. This young rabbi gave me the green light to scratch that spiritual itch while viewing religion on my terms.

My second spiritual pillar comes from the intersection of skepticism and the limitations of the human language. We embrace and pay homage to the unknown. And we reject the false choice about the universe that some of us choose to buy into.

So what do I mean by this "false choice?" The idea that science and religion are at complete odds with each other. That either you believe in science or you believe in religion, but that you cannot do both. I now wholeheartedly reject that line of thinking. In fact, it is precisely because I *do* believe in science that I have now concluded there must be a God.

Stay with me on this. No matter what angle you are coming from, there will always be big existential questions we cannot answer. Ever. And as it pertains to Liz and me, it means that despite all the wonderful medical support and science at our disposal, at some point the science runs out of answers and we are forced to confront the unknown. Liz likens this sensation to standing at the end of a cliff and leaping, unsure whether you will plummet or soar. It's the moment when, to put it nicely, shit gets real.

This moment on the edge of the cliff, for us, is where faith comes in. It's played a big role in my worldview, and it's played an especially big role in being caregiver to Liz. Because again, science does not have all the answers. In fact, in some ways, there are more questions than answers. We will probably never know how any of this happened to us. Nor will we likely ever know, with total certainty, that cancer is permanently behind us.

And so our faith is the deep, abiding belief that no matter how frightening the moment or harrowing the statistics, there is a happy conclusion for us. It is embracing humility and ultimately being at peace with the unknown and the unknowable. It is the belief that we are guided by a benevolent power even if we cannot begin to comprehend—much less fully explain—what that power is. This faith gives us stability and comfort.

But it's not just about Liz's health. That's just the tip of the iceberg. Faith has universal application. Because Liz's health isn't the only thing in life beyond our control or beyond explanation, whether by the scientific method or otherwise. To use a big existential example, how it is that any of us are even here in the world? Because no matter how far we humans attempt to trace back to the "origin" of the universe in terms of the science, we eventually run out of answers.

You say it all started with the big bang? Great! But how did that happen? Where did the energy or the dust particles or whatever come from that made the big bang possible? How did *that* all begin? Is there even such a thing as a "beginning"? I've yet to see a scientific consensus on an answer to those questions. At some point, if you keep drilling, you end up at "no one knows."

So here is what you are left with. There is *something* out there—an unknown "it"—that just *is*. And always was. And always will be. Call it whatever you like and worship it (or not) however you choose, but it is—and will remain—a permanent anchor for Liz and me. The leap of faith.

This "call it whatever you like" part is key. It's funny... I've had lots of deep conversations over the years with people who claim to not believe in God, but who subscribe to the idea of karma. Or fate. Or some other cosmic force. In those discussions, I don't think our differences are theological. They're more semantical.

Our terminology may be different, but at bottom we are both saying we believe in the idea of a higher power of sorts. We're just calling it by a different name and setting up different belief systems around it.

So that's it. I believe that this unknown, unknowable "it" force is benevolent and I choose to worship it. It gives me inner comfort and adds balance and humility to my life. That is what it comes down to. That's my case for God.

And since I have indulged myself with the freedom to take the scriptures seriously but not literally, I can tailor my religion and religious practices to my liking. They are guided by Jewish tradition and informed by Jewish values, but in no way ensnared by all the complications and politics of organized religion. In short, I've made my faith practice *mine*, and because we're an interfaith family, it is perhaps better said that Liz and I have made it *ours*.

This process of creating a shared spiritual space has been a powerful experience for us. It was a path we were already on before Liz's diagnosis, and I repeat that point because faith has meant so much more to us than just finding comfort in a crisis. Of course, faith serves that purpose for us also, but that's only a piece of it if we're truly living life to the fullest.

There's something really cool and humbling about being part of a bigger tradition and history that passes down centuries from generation to generation. The songs and the rituals. Heck, even the smells (if you've ever been to a Hanukkah party where someone is cooking potato latkes, you know exactly what I'm talking about). There's so much richness in the overall fabric to choose from. So we pick our spots and lean on the things that speak to us. But we do it on our terms.

Take the High Holidays. This is the Jewish New Year and, eight days later, the Day of Atonement. These days call for a lot of standing in prayer in synagogue while reading solemn-sounding liturgy. If I'm being totally honest, it can be a grind. But instead of just "checking the box" after sitting through a boring service at the synagogue and calling it a day, we use the time for earnest self-reflection.

So this is the Day of Atonement. What can I focus on for myself for this upcoming year? Are there things this past year I wish I had done better or differently? How can I be a better version of myself?

We make this a shared experience. Liz and I will share our personal, individual goals for the upcoming year, and then we will check in from time to time over the ensuing months to reflect on our progress. We'll laugh, cry, and exchange high-fives. It's our form of accountability, loving and without judgment.

But at the end of the day, it always comes back to my prior discussion about faith and gratitude being so tightly intertwined. That's really the centerpiece. Like how Liz and I took a traditionally Jewish ritual of Shabbat and riffed it into something more uniquely ours by making the thankfulness part the most important feature. We now look at every holiday and milestone through this lens.

Something I wrote in late 2021, as I was pondering all of this:

There's a prayer known as a Shehecheyanu. It is recited to commemorate "special occasions" like graduations, weddings, births, new homes, job promotions, and all manner of other milestone-y stuff. It's a way to pause and say thanks for the big moment. Most Jews will say it countless times over the course of a life.

While I've always loved the idea of this ritual, there's a part of me these days that has questions I'd not considered before. Among other things, I wonder if whether by placing so much of an emphasis on the big milestones we are undervaluing all of the little treasured moments along the way.

And this is why our weekly Friday Shabbat ritual is so important to our family. Because while the big moments are great, if you're not saying thanks for all the (seemingly) little stuff in between the big Shehecheyanu moments, you're missing out on a full appreciation for the blessing of life itself. Certainly for most of us, there are many, many more "little" moments than "big" ones. And while it's obviously not practical to literally stop and say thanks after every mundane incident over the course of a day, I'd argue that it is equally prob-

lematic to never acknowledge those moments at all. And overlooking that problem of overlooking is an easy habit to fall into.

Faith, just like thankfulness, is an everyday practice.

So there you have it. Thankfulness and faith, knotted together. Far beyond just carrying us through a time of crisis, it has enriched us and added deeper meaning to our lives. We believe, we have faith, and then we stop to consciously say thanks for the nourishment it provides. We may not do it all literally and by the book, but we are serious about it and do it in a way that speaks to us.

An indispensable part of the journey.

Chapter 17
A Closing Note About Closure

THANK GOD FOR TODAY. Tomorrow? Still lots of unknowns.

One of the tougher concepts in my ongoing journey into spirituality and stoicism is this idea of closure. We're hardwired to want it and it is ever-present in our culture: in movies, stories, sports, and songs. Things in life have finite boundaries, and final scores, and beginnings and ends. We conclude, we accept the results, we move on.

But real life doesn't always go that way. It has uncertainties and jagged edges and open boundaries. It can be messy. And it can be highly unsettling to not get in your life what you've been programmed to expect as a given. Doubly so when the uncertainty comes in the form of a dangerous and highly unpredictable disease. It's not like breaking an arm, where they take the cast off after a few months and then the episode settles down into a historical life event. The threat lingers.

Although much of this book has been about exercising every bit of my internal fortitude to remain thankful and positive, the journey has also come with moments of emotional crisis. At points during every stage—from initial diagnosis to recovery to living in the here and now—I've bottomed out in occasional episodes of hopelessness and despair. The looming questions surrounding Liz's health are weights we may never get to put down, and sometimes we are overwhelmed by the ramifications of that. Liz describes it as a "smoldering fear" in our lives, and that's as good a description as any that I have been able to come up with.

And sometimes—not frequently, but sometimes—I still to this day struggle to make my peace with it.

We are, of course, buoyed by all the support and take comfort in knowing we have beaten all statistical odds for a few years running. That's been nothing short of a miracle and we are thankful for it.

But even so, it often feels unsettling and unfair that we can't bank on getting to grow old together. On travelling to all the places we scratched out on that rumpled old napkin. On watching our young boys become young men. On doing all the things we've been dreaming about doing since we locked hands and decided to experience all the joys and adventures of life together. We yearn for a closure we may never get.

But here's where the stoics and the religious scholars get it right. Amidst all the unknowns and ugly statistics and uncertainty and chaos, what we do have—always—is total control of our appreciation for this very moment. And this one. And this one, too. We have the eternal blessings of faith, and gratitude, and love. We have the memories we've made. My goodness, we've been fortunate.

Nothing can take that away from us.

***

A final story from our journey. At the time Liz was diagnosed, we were two months shy of our ten-year wedding anniversary. Until our life took its unexpected turn, we were planning a big party to celebrate the occasion. We had already paid deposits for a venue and a live band. We had a contract in place for a food truck and a heavy box of invitations was sitting on our dining room table, patiently waiting to be addressed, stamped, and dropped in the mail.

And then the phone call that changed everything. I emailed vendors to cancel our orders. Our invitations never left the box.

But as the weeks went by and our anniversary crept closer, we decided ten years was too important a milestone to just let go by altogether. So we pivoted. We gathered our immediate family and headed down to the little park that sits at the end of our street. And then, before God, and the Rabbi, and our children, we renewed our vows and re-affirmed our eternal commitment to one another. We clasped our hands in prayer.

The sun shined overhead.

A quiet, subdued affair. So very different from what we had originally planned. But so much more meaningful.

Yes, life is messy and rough and unpredictable, but I wouldn't trade it for any other. Jagged edges and all. You breathe in, you breathe out, and you say a prayer of gratitude. Hopefully, you connect with the feeling and mean it. And then, filled with all that grace and wonder... you look forward.

And you breathe in again.

Acknowledgements

AMONG THE MANY THINGS being a caregiver has taught me is the importance of leaning into the ol' support network. This isn't just platitude; I truly wouldn't have made it through the past few years without an extensive group of family and friends who helped me keep my head above water during the most difficult moments. I'm ever thankful for the opportunity to acknowledge many of those folks now.

I have to start with my wife Elizabeth, who is the center of my universe and who plays the most important role in our story. I've had a ringside seat to witness in amazement your unmatched courage, strength, and grace. Let's do this thing of ours forever, my love. We got this.

I need to thank our boys, too—Eli and Isaac—for serving as the inspiration for me to take care of my mental health once things became really terrifying, and for bringing a daily blast of sunshine and joy to my life. You're both way too young for the subject matter here, though, so hopefully we are years away from you guys actually reading this shout-out. Just know that no matter where life leads us, Daddy will be there for you.

To Liz's Mom, Nancy Ballard. You are a rock. I think we all know where Liz's courage and strength and grace come from. Thank you for divvying up the night shifts at Emory with me and for everything else you have done for Liz, me, and the boys. On Friday nights, we often light candles and say a prayer of thanks for you. You deserve as many vacations as your busy retirement schedule allows.

That goes for the rest of our family. The parents and step-parents, our siblings, and all the rest of our crazy crew of aunts, uncles, and cousins. You helped guide us through the treatment options that eventually led us to the medical experts (my Dad and Aunt He), pampered Liz during her lengthy hospitalization (Liz's sister, Marie), cared for the boys when Liz and I desperately needed rest (my Mother and my sister, Kim), and appeared on our doorstep to serve up much-needed cheer and laughter during our post-surgery freefall (Cousin Laurie aka Aunt Banana). And you were always available to listen to us labor our way through the hard stuff (Jimbo, Ruth, and Aunt Holly), which is every bit as important as all the other help we were getting.

Man, it's getting misty in here.

And then there's our dear friends Lauren Estrin and Andy Deutsch, our non-family member MVPs. My goodness, where to start? Before Liz was diagnosed, Estrin would sometimes joke that she'd be willing to lie down in Atlanta traffic for Liz if she had to. Turns out she meant it. You guys have this ability to magically appear at every key moment to offer help when we need it the most. Team QuaranTEAM forever.

To the Jacksons: Luke, Kristin and family. You guys are a pretty indispensable part of this journey, too. Extra thanks to Kristin for basically being Liz's own personal nurse on call. We love you guys.

Heartfelt shout-outs also to the other families who loved and cared for our boys when I was away and tethered to Liz's side: Mark and Emily Rogers, Prinz and Elena Pinakatt, and Bryan and Lauren Ruchin. There weren't a lot of humorous moments when Liz and I were enjoying our extended stay at Emory Hospital, but watching you guys jostle and maneuver via text message over who got to entertain Eli and Isaac on weekend afternoons was definitely one of them. I cannot imagine a greater, more important *mitzvah* than the one you performed.

And speaking of *mitzvahs*: Rabbi Berg and the rest of the clergy and staff at the Temple. They offer prayer and comfort in the synagogue, at the hospital, in your home, over cocktails (really), via emails and text messages, and in every other venue and medium you can think of in the space-time continuum. They are always there and they are never short on time, even with their own home lives and families to tend to. Nobody does it better.

Next acknowledgment is for my law partners (current and recently departed), my legal assistant Joanne, and the rest of my colleagues at Balch. Lots of law firms like to talk about engendering a family-like culture, but you guys have walked the walk for well over two decades now. Thanks for getting on flights to attend far-flung depositions in my stead, for raising a ton of money for cancer research, and for taking lots and lots of arrows for me while I was gone. Also, for not making me feel weird about having my occasional moments. Said in the most benign, non- actionable-under-Title VII kind of way: I love you guys.

As for the process of book-writing itself, I've been blessed to have some mega-talented, creative friends who have been suggesting for years that I needed to channel my artistic side and find something to write about. While I don't think this was the subject matter any of us had in mind, I can't thank you enough for the advice and kind words of encouragement throughout this project: Jed Broitman, Sean Daniels, and Kevin Gillese. I finally did it! (But I'm still totally going to start a blog about the intersection of politics and parenting one day, damnit). And special thanks also to the professional writers who took the time to offer advice and to help explain the business and mechanical parts of the trade: Doron Levine, Whitney Fleming, Dallas Taylor, David Marmins, Riv Begun, Zoe Fishman Schacham, Rich Oelberger, and Jes Landau.

A few other acknowledgements to an important group of dear friends—some new, some old—who helped shine light on the path about us, who provided perspective and counsel, or even just took the time to sit with me out in the Emory Hospital parking lot when I desperately needed the company: Brian Seinberg, Cherie Simon, Scott Zweigel, Scott Chalk, Shawn and Melissa Baldwin, Alison Clark, Greg Michell, Alyssa Philips, Averi Magnuson, Bob and Patti Cross, Joey and Nikki Tessler, Dan and Meredith Kingsley, and Patrick and Jenny Hergenrother. Legends, all of you.

To Stuart: Eternal thanks, from Liz and me.

To Dr. Charles Staley. It's not often you get to use the word "lifesaver" in the literal sense, but with you there is no more apt description. If there's ever a movement to re-name every single building on Emory's campus after you, Liz and I will spearhead it. God bless you, along with the rest of your miracle-working team of doctors, nurses, and administrators. Thank you also to Dr. Dipen Parekh (University of Miami Health System) and our next-door neighbor, Dr. Constance Harrell Shreckengost (Emory U), for helping us find and make contact with Dr. Staley so quickly. Our story does not play out this way without the world-class medical attention we received.

Finally, a warm shout-out to my publisher, Jason Cannon at Ibis Books. Thanks for appreciating the importance of sharing our story and for having the vision to help make that actually happen.

Also, for having the skill to give really good notes to a guy (that would be me) who can sometimes be a little precious about his own writing. I've learned an awful lot from you in a short amount of time. You are a true *mensch*, man.

About the Author

Matthew Ames is a husband and father of two. He is also a partner at an Atlanta law firm, where he handles complex business disputes. He has been recognized as a Georgia Super Lawyer for several years running and was selected by his peers for inclusion in the 2023 edition of *The Best Lawyers in America*. In addition to his law practice, Matt previously served as Board Chair at a local arts organization and has also served on the boards of several Atlanta non-profit organizations. On most weekends, you can find Matt and the light of his life, Liz, cheering wildly for their boys out on the soccer pitch. *Through the Impossible* is his first book.

Made in the USA
Columbia, SC
06 November 2023

25574516R00124